BLAIRSVILLE SENIOR HIGH SCHOOL
BLAIRSVILLE, PENNA.

DATE DUE

OCT 22	APR 5		
NOV 5			
NOV 17	APR 17		
DEC 17	DEC 14		
FEB 8	JAN 31		
MAR 1	JAN 30		
MAR 10	JAN 22		
	FEB 13		
MAR 27	FEB 25		
MAR 24	APR 16		
APR 14	FEB 9		
MAY 17	teacher		
MAY 18	SEP 29 '83		
JAN 4	1-28-87		
JAN 17	DEC 02 1999		
APR 12			
SEP 23			
OCT 6			
NOV 10			
GAYLORD		PRINTED IN U.S.A.

THE FIRST TEXAS RANGER
Jack Hays

BORN: JANUARY 28, 1817
DIED: APRIL 21, 1883

Nineteen-year-old Jack Hays, Tennessean by
birth, volunteer in the Texas army, was one
of the bravest soldiers in the struggle for
Texas independence. With the threat of a
new invasion from Mexico, he was given
permission to form his own frontier company—and the Texas Rangers was born. In
the years that followed, Jack Hays and his
Texas Rangers became one of the most
important and effective law-enforcement
bodies in the West. When Texas joined the
Union, the famed Rangers became a regiment in the regular army, where Hays
served for many years.

Books by Curtis Bishop

THE FIRST TEXAS RANGER
Jack Hays

LONE STAR LEADER
Sam Houston

THE FIRST
TEXAS RANGER

Jack Hays

★

by CURTIS BISHOP

JULIAN MESSNER, INC. · NEW YORK

Published by Julian Messner, Inc.
8 West 40 Street, New York 18

Published simultaneously in Canada
by The Copp Clark Publishing Co. Limited

Second Printing, 1962

Printed in the United States of America

Library of Congress Catalog Card No. 59-12755

To

JOE AUSTELL SMALL

He made a dream of the WEST *come* TRUE

Contents

Contents

1

One More Volunteer for Texas

One look at the approaching horseman was enough for nine-year-old Bobbie Hays.

"Sarah, Sarah!" the boy shouted. "Come quick. It's Jack!"

Sarah came hurriedly out of the house, a disapproving scowl on her face. A sister older by two full years felt duty-bound to discourage such wild claims.

"You're seeing things," she scolded. "Jack is at the Academy and . . ." Her voice faded off into a gasp, then sounded again as an excited squeal. "It *is* Jack!"

And without heeding young Bobbie's cries of "Wait for me," she ran to the gate to meet her brother. By the time the rider's feet touched the ground, she had thrown her arms around him tightly and Bobbie was fiercely hugging his knees.

From the porch Robert Cage, uncle and legal guardian of the trio, watched with mixed emotions. For four years he had treated Sarah and Bobbie as tenderly as if they were his own children. He had tried just as hard to be a second father to Jack Hays too, but he knew he had not succeeded.

Jack lacked only months of reaching his twentieth year, but still he was no larger than most half-grown boys. His

small stature had been one of the chief reasons why Robert
Cage had discouraged his nephew's ambitions to become a
surveyor or a soldier. Fighting men, Cage believed, should
be big men. An almost full-grown man who was below
average in height, and slim besides, should work toward
a career in business or a profession.

When Jack finally freed himself of the embraces of his
younger sister and brother, he stepped up to the porch,
his hand outstretched.

"How are you, Uncle Robert?" he asked.

"Welcome, Jack, welcome," Cage said heartily.

Neither of the younger Hays children sensed any strain
between their brother and uncle. The disagreement between Robert Cage and his nephew dated back four years,
longer than either Bobbie or Sarah could remember. The
breach had been healed to the extent that Jack felt welcome to visit his brother and sister, and did so at every
chance; but he considered himself only a guest at the
Mississippi plantation, not a ward nor a dependent. And
he was treated as a guest too. Not since Jack's fifteenth
year had his uncle accepted any responsibility for his
actions.

Mrs. Cage greeted Jack warmly too. She listened eagerly
to news about relatives in Tennessee, then bustled off to
oversee preparations for dinner. Bobbie and Sarah were
persuaded to play outside a while, leaving uncle and
nephew to themselves.

As he and Robert Cage settled themselves in the parlor,
Jack wondered whether he should tell his uncle about his
plans. He had given considerable thought to that question
on the long ride from Nashville to Yazoo City. His Tennessee relatives knew where he was going and why. Most
of them approved of his decision too. He was young and

vigorous. He was the son of Harmon Hays, who had fought against the Creeks and whose Tennessee company had manned the center line at the Battle of New Orleans. Jack was a nephew by marriage of Andrew Jackson, "Old Hickory." As a small boy he had been a favorite of Sam Houston, "The Raven." In a generation's time his father's family had helped tame two frontiers and wage two wars against the British. The Tennessee branch of the family understood why he was eager to reach Texas and swap shots with General Santa Anna's soldiers.

But Robert Cage neither understood nor appreciated such a love for adventure and the outdoors. The planter, accepting the custody of the three Hays children in the best of faith when fever took the lives of their parents, planned their future carefully. Mr. Cage had wanted Jack to become a businessman, and intended to establish this nephew in a business of his own as soon as he was old enough. Until that time Jack would serve an apprenticeship with a Yazoo City merchant. But the boy had rebelled.

He wanted to be a soldier and a surveyor, not a merchant. He wanted to finish his studies at Davidson Academy and then apply for an appointment to West Point. When Mr. Cage insisted that Jack follow his plan instead, the youth left his uncle's home and found a job with a surveyor's gang. By the time he was sixteen, Jack was running his own lines in the Mississippi woods and collecting his own fees. Although legally he was still Jack's guardian, Mr. Cage did not try to interfere.

After lighting his pipe and settling himself in his favorite chair, Mr. Cage looked at his nephew and said slowly, "I take it that you have withdrawn from the Academy?"

"Yes, sir," Jack answered promptly, his hazel eyes meeting his uncle's look squarely.

"And spent most of your savings on a horse and pistols?" The older man had noticed these new items at once. Jack had ridden up on a stout chestnut stallion which showed some thoroughbred blood. And his silver-butted pistols still showed their newness.

"Yes, sir," he said again.

"What now?" asked the planter. "More surveying? You have established a good reputation in this neighborhood. Judge Patterson asked about you last week. He said you were the most dependable man with a chain around here."

Jack smiled. He appreciated this compliment from such a qualified man. It proved how well he had done. When he had first started surveying, land traders had been reluctant to hire such a young man.

"I don't think," he said hesitantly, "I'll be doing any more surveying. At least not for a while."

"You should think twice before trying something else," Mr. Cage said with a disapproving frown. "It's hardly good business to leap from one thing to another and from one place to another. I'd hate to see you throw away the opportunity you have here."

His tone settled Jack's doubts. He would not discuss his plans, for his uncle was simply not in sympathy with his spirit. An argument about the wisdom of his decision would serve no good purpose. So, Jack decided, he would not mention the subject of Texas.

Bobbie burst into the room before Jack could be pressed further about his plans.

"Didn't you kill an Indian when you were just sixteen?" demanded the boy. "Didn't you now?"

"Yes. Why?"

Sarah came right on her brother's heels.

"Tommy Lester says you didn't," she said indignantly. "He says Bobbie and I just made that story up."

"I'm a little curious about that story myself," said Mr. Cage. "I didn't hear it until last winter. I didn't know until then that my own nephew had driven the last hostile Choctaws out of this country."

"I'm not sure that we drove them anywhere," Jack said truthfully. "The last I saw of them, George Work and I were running off and leaving them. And mighty glad to get away too."

Mrs. Cage came in to say that dinner was ready, but she joined the others in insisting that Jack tell the story first.

"Well," he said reluctantly, "George and I were out running a line. It was an out-of-the-way location, in pretty wild country. These Choctaws passed us, and we noticed that they didn't look very friendly. After a while they turned around and started following us. George didn't have a gun and all I had was a single-shot pistol. There were eight or nine of them, so we didn't want any trouble.

"We decided pretty quickly to let the surveying go and get out of there. But when we started running, the Choctaws came after us that much harder. One of them had a faster horse than the others—faster than either of ours too. He caught up with us pretty quick and shot George's horse. I jumped out of the saddle, gave George my horse, and hid behind some rocks. When I saw the Choctaw heading for George with his tomahawk ready, I yelled for George to use his rope, and he did it just right. That sort of flustered the Indian, having a rope around him. While he was trying to untangle it, I shot him in the head. He toppled to the ground. I leapfrogged up on his horse and we started running again. They never caught up with us, and that was the last we saw of them." He smiled faintly and added, "We didn't want to see them again either."

"Well, Indian fighters have to eat, and dinner is ready," his aunt said briskly. "Come along, Jack. I don't know whether Bobbie will let you get enough to eat or not. He is eating like a horse these days."

"Good," said Jack, patting the boy's brother. "Let's hope he doesn't grow up to be a runt like his big brother."

"When you have a gun in your hand," Bobbie said proudly, "you're bigger than anybody. You were bigger than that Choctaw chief, weren't you?"

"I don't know that he was a chief, Bobbie," Jack objected.

"Sure he was," the boy insisted. "I just know he was."

"Well, chief or not, I was glad to see him dead and to get away from his friends," the older brother replied quietly.

During dinner Bobbie turned to Jack and said firmly, "You'd be bigger than old Santa Anna and those Mexicans in Texas, too. I just wish I was big enough to help get even with them for what they did at the Alamo."

Jack shot an anxious glance at his uncle. He was sorry Bobbie had mentioned Texas, a subject he certainly did not want to discuss with Mr. Cage. But the older man was apparently paying little attention to Bobbie's chatter.

"Tommy Lester's bragging all over the country that his big brother is going to fight the Mexicans," Sarah put in, her voice scornful. "He's going with General Huston. But I don't see why that's anything for Tommy to brag about."

Mr. Cage stirred in his chair and seemed about to say something to Jack, but before he could speak his wife said, "Come, Sarah, help me start clearing the table; and you Bobbie, see to your evening chores. I want to get through

Another party fell in with them as they forded the Sabine. They were over ninety strong when they rode into Nacogdoches.

Jack's eyes lighted up when he sighted the village ahead. The Texas settlement, he was sure, would welcome them enthusiastically—ninety fighting men, already armed, asking for nothing but a "crack at the Mexicans!" They expected a welcome like that given David Crockett and his Tennessee volunteers at every Texas town—singing, speeches, free whisky in the town square. If it was true that Sam Houston had less than four hundred men ready to fight, these newcomers might well be the salvation of the Texas cause.

But no huzzahs sounded; no overjoyed citizens rushed to meet them. Instead, they found Nacogdoches overrun with able-bodied men who apparently had nothing to do. And every eye that Jack Hays met flashed suspicion and resentment of the new arrivals.

"Lordee," exclaimed Jeremiah Bain, a bearded Kentuckian who had earned Jack's friendship and respect in these days of travel. "Who said Texas needed volunteers? There are more here than you can shake a stick at."

Jack nodded, as puzzled as Bain.

Another Kentuckian who had established himself as unofficial leader of the party reined up before a blacksmith shop to ask a few questions.

"You jaspers might as well take it easy," he was told. "The shooting's all over."

"What do you mean?"

"Just that. If you come here just for the fighting, you might as well head back to where you came from. The shooting's over, and if there's anything we don't need in Texas, it's half-starved human wolves on the prowl."

so that I can talk to Jack some more about the folks in Tennessee."

Bless her, thought Jack. She must have seen how badly he wanted to change the subject. He knew how all southern Mississippi had seethed with excitement over the massacre of Americans at the Alamo and Goliad in Texas. He had heard, too, that Felix Huston, who owned a plantation near the Cages, planned to organize and equip a volunteer company at his own expense. Uncle Robert would not approve of Jack's going to Texas at all. But if he were to reveal his intentions, his uncle would want him to accompany General Huston, a man of means and influence. Huston would certainly be willing to enlist Jack Hays, the young surveyor and Indian fighter. But Jack had his own plans, and he did not want an argument with his uncle about them.

To the youth's relief, there was no further mention of Texas again that night. And Robert Cage was neither surprised nor regretful the next morning when a servant discovered Jack's farewell notes, one addressed to Mr. Cage, the other to his brother and sister. Apparently the young guest had risen before daylight and quietly taken his leave.

Both notes told his purpose—to cross the Sabine River and join the Texas Revolutionary Army. But his message for Bobbie and Sarah held a promise that neither one revealed to their guardians. Someday, Jack said, he would see that they joined him in Texas.

Robert Cage was right. There was no holding back the son of Harmon Hays and favorite nephew of Andrew Jackson. Jack Hays had already traveled several miles before daylight on that morning of April 19, 1836. And most certainly he was heading for Texas to join Sam Houston's volunteer army.

Sam Houston! The name brought back all sorts of boyhood memories. . . . Harmon Hays had settled with his bride on a plantation at Little Cedar Lick, Tennessee. Their second child, born on January 27, 1817, had been named John Coffee Hays, for General John Coffee, a valiant commander against both the British and the Creek Indians. Not far from the Hays plantation stood the stately Jackson mansion, "The Hermitage." As a child, Jack had romped on its broad lawns, had sat spellbound on its wide portico and listened to the talk of General Andrew Jackson's former lieutenants. None of them had impressed him more than Sam Houston, "Old Hickory's" chosen successor as governor of Tennessee.

Now this same Sam Houston commanded a small, nondescript army that needed help desperately. Reports from west of the Sabine River were confused and irregular, but their grim tone never changed. General Houston had only a few hundred followers and no artillery, while Santa Anna, the Mexican dictator, boasted several thousand trained troops and all the war matériel he needed. Along almost every trail leading to Nacogdoches, the gateway to Texas, plodded horsemen who wanted to strike a blow for freedom in Texas. But would enough of them get there in time?

Just after daylight Jack came upon three other young men riding West, and quickly accepted their invitation to share a meager breakfast and travel on in their company. About mid-morning they overtook a party of six and joined forces. When they camped for the night beside a sluggish creek, their number had grown to twenty.

Not all of them were desirable companions, and Jack slept with his pistols lying beside him. He had little money —it had taken nearly all his savings to buy his horse, pistols, and bowie knife—but most of these Texas-bound men were

poorer than he. Some rode mules or bony mares and had only squirrel guns and knives for weapons. A handsome mount and new pistols were sure to tempt many of them.

Jack had associated with rough men before; thus their presence did not daunt him. He had held his own with more dangerous characters in the Mississippi woods. And he quickly sensed the purpose of Cal Puckett, who rolled out his blanket only an arm's length away. Jack pretended to be sleeping soundly, but lay waiting. A faint stirring gave warning that Puckett was reaching toward him. Jack raised one of his pistols.

"Looking for something?" he asked softly.

Puckett blustered for an instant. "Rock's bothering me," he finally muttered. "Can't get comfortable."

He turned his back toward Jack and in a few moments moved his bedroll farther away.

The volunteers swam their horses across the Mississippi River and entered New Orleans. Some went into the city to look up the committee of merchants who were encouraging the cause of Texas freedom. Adolphus Sterne, William P. Christy, and others would provide a rifle and a new homespun suit for any able-bodied man going across the Sabine. But Jack did not want or need such gifts; he was eager to push on. Rumors in New Orleans of a battle pending between Houston's band and Santa Anna's force added to his impatience. The provisional President of the Texas Republic, David G. Burnet, had ordered Houston to fight or to quit as commander. There was sure to be action soon, and Jack did not want to miss it.

Jack soon found new companions—a party of fifty-one Kentuckians—with whom to continue his journey. A group of twenty Louisianans overtook them at Natchitoches.

In snatches, in the rough language of frontiersmen, the latest party of volunteers heard about Sam Houston's sweeping victory at San Jacinto.

Santa Anna and sixteen hundred followers had been attacked during the *siesta* hour on April 21. The Texas force of seven hundred men had captured or killed the entire invading army, including the dictator himself. Sam Houston had been wounded and was traveling by boat to New Orleans for medical treatment. The Texas army was completely disorganized, without a foe, without a commander. The Texas government was a joke. Nobody knew where President Burnet was and nobody cared. Some high-falutin poetry writer named Mirabeau B. Lamar was trying to run the army, but nobody paid him any mind. The merchants in Texas was plumb disgusted with the riffraff pouring across the Sabine to muscle in on the spoils. The newcomers had better show cash money or they'd face some lean days in the new country.

Jack listened in disappointment and disgust. What a fine climax! The revolution already won and new volunteers unwelcome! Houston already victorious! Jack recalled his days of travel from Nashville to Yazoo City to Nacogdoches. If he had not turned off to visit his younger brother and sister, he might have reached Texas in time for the action . . .

Then he put aside such moody reflections with a shrug. That couldn't be helped now. He was in Texas and the next thing to do was to see about finding a place for himself. Besides, how could he have left on such a long journey without seeing Bobbie and Sarah?

"If I had any cash," Jeremiah Bain muttered, "I'd get good and drunk. I'd get as drunk as a hoot owl."

"I'll at least buy you a drink," offered Jack. "In a saloon we can find out more about what's happened anyhow."

"Then let's wet our whistle," said the Kentuckian. "I don't know what we'll find out, though. 'Pears to me we're stuck in the wrong place at the wrong time."

They had to push their way into the packed saloon, and the other customers made room for them reluctantly.

"Let's see your money," the bartender said suspiciously when they ordered a drink.

Jack pulled a gold coin out of his pocket. With a satisfied nod the barkeep set out two glasses.

"Here's to the Republic of Texas," the youth said to Bain. He and the Kentuckian raised their glasses——

There was a crash as Jack's glass splintered into a thousand pieces on the saloon floor. Towering over the youth, a burly black-bearded man glared at him belligerently. "You don't drink no toast like that, young 'un," he challenged. "You didn't have nuthin' to do with it. Puny whippersnappers like you didn't whip the Mexicans. And just pull out one of them fancy pistols of yours if you don't cotton to my style. I double-dog-dare you."

As he finished speaking he reached for his gun, and his push sent Jack reeling backward.

Jack had been schooled by expert duelists in a quick aim and fast shooting. In addition, he had won every marksmanship match at the Academy. Now, he did not flinch or hesitate. He jerked out his pistol and shot in the same motion. His adversary never got a chance to fire back.

Jack's bullet thudded into the bearded bully's chest. The dark-faced man froze in his tracks. He wavered off-balance for a moment, then pitched forward on his face.

"Lordee!" gasped Bain. "You plugged him center."

The unexpected shot silenced the saloon's bedlam. Every

eye stared at the slim youth quietly replacing his pistol in his belt.

"You Georgia crackers have been asking for trouble all day," croaked a gaunt, red-haired man. "Maybe now you won't be so rambunctious."

Jack turned to the bartender. "It was self-defense," he said quietly. "I'm willing to surrender to any legal authority."

"Send for Clarkson," suggested one awed spectator. "He was the *alcalde* under Mexican law. Reckon he's still in charge."

Clarkson proved to be a swarthy, heavy-set blacksmith. He listened gravely to Jack's account of the shooting, then questioned a few bystanders. No witness challenged the youth's statements: the dead man had launched an unprovoked attack.

Clarkson shrugged his broad shoulders. "No call for me to butt in," he said. "But if you've got a place to go, youngster, I'd get moving. There'll be nothing but trouble around here until this pack of drifters moves on. Trouble always comes in bunches too. You got any plans?"

Jack shook his head. His only reason for coming to Texas had been to enlist in the army, he explained.

"That ain't easy to do right now," Clarkson told him. "Nobody is sure of the authority to sign you up or to give you orders. Any friends you could look up?"

Jack thought a moment. There was General Houston, of course, but the wounded soldier was sailing to New Orleans. Besides, he did not intend to trade on Houston's reputation. Or on his uncle's either. He could stand on his own in Texas.

"Some friends of my family settled on the Brazos River," Jack recalled. "They came with Stephen F. Austin."

"Then look 'em up," advised the *alcalde*. "Stay with 'em until things settle down. You're too nice a youngster to be mixed up in barroom didoes. There won't be nuthin' done about this ruckus, I'll promise that. But be careful, youngster. You'll get along in Texas if you'll just remember to be careful. You ain't big, but you pack the difference in your belt there. So long."

Jack, accepting the blacksmith's counsel, rode on to the American colonies established several years earlier. Near the settlement of Washington-on-the-Brazos, Isaac Donahoe, an old friend of the Hays family, gave him a warm welcome. Donahoe showed him the frame shed where the Texans had met two months ago to draft their Declaration of Independence.

"Right there she was," he said proudly, pointing to the shed. "Just a bunch of galoots the same as you and me. They stayed thirsty all the time they were here and never got enough to eat. But before they pulled out they had started us a country here, our own country. What they started, Houston finished. A Tennessean wrote the declaration, George Childress. A Tennessean won the war for us—Burnet, all he did was yap—Houston did the fighting.

"Tom Rusk will take a letter from me and put you to doing something. Rusk is no politician: he's a man that gets things done. Once they were all talking, the powers-that-be, about how bad things looked. Rusk just yawned in their faces. 'Let's go have a drink,' he said, 'and fight our way out of this mess. That's the only way out, fighting. We could talk here a year without getting a thing accomplished.' That's Tom Rusk for you. They call him Secretary of War now, but I don't figure he's much of a secretary. He's a leader, like Houston. Like your father was. I'll write you a letter to Tom Rusk."

Two days later Jack Hays rode along the *camino real* to the shabby headquarters of the Texas military command. The soldiers had refused to take orders from Mirabeau B. Lamar, and General Tom Rusk had accepted temporary command of the volunteers. But he could not pay his men, nor could he discipline them. Those who had farms to look after went home without a by-your-leave from anyone. Those who had no place to go hung around camp, quarreling, gambling.

General Rusk pointed out these conditions to the new volunteer.

"I'll sign you up," he said wearily, "but I can't guarantee ever to pay you. I'll give you a job to do, but I can't make you take orders."

Jack chose not to let such points bother him. With little ceremony he was sworn into the services of the Texas Republic. The date was May 14, 1836; he was only nineteen.

2

Jack Makes a Pact with Sam Houston

Jack Hays carefully scraped the October mud from his boots before entering the small frame building which served as the capitol of the new Republic of Texas. He could have saved himself at least some of his trouble, for the offices of the Chief Executive were neither neat nor impressive. A two-room box residence of pine plank had been converted to the use of Sam Houston, first President of the new republic. The little settlement of Columbia had been selected as the seat of the government when residents there offered to furnish this and two other structures, equally small and plain, as "official buildings."

W. D. Miller, Houston's secretary, was suspicious of the young visitor.

"If you're here about bounty lands," Miller said in a weary voice, "the President can't help you. We can't issue land certificates until Congress meets and passes the necessary legislation."

Jack shook his head. The men who enlisted in the Texan army had been promised free tracts of land. Most of them wanted their farms immediately and were impatient with government delay. But Jack Hays had learned in his surveying experience that it took time to open a new country to settlement. He had not come about lands.

"I'm John Coffee Hays," he told the secretary. "General Houston told General Rusk that he wanted to see me."

"Oh," said Miller in a more friendly tone. "I'll tell the President, but there will be some delay anyhow. Please have a chair."

Jack accepted one of the straight-backed, cane-bottomed chairs. In a few minutes the secretary returned with word that Sam Houston would see him shortly.

The President's invitation had reached Jack Hays through General Rusk himself. At least twice in the months since May, Sam Houston had heard something of the youthful volunteer. The first time was in the report, written by Jack, on the burial of the Goliad victims. General Rusk had ordered Christian burial for the 350 men slain in the mission massacre early in June. Some time later Hays had accompanied a detail which slaughtered wild cattle to feed the idle Texan army, and again it was he who wrote the official report. General Rusk had recommended the young Tennessean to the new President. From this recommendation Houston first learned that the son of his old friend Harmon Hays was in the Texan ranks.

The presidential summons followed, and there, in Columbia, Jack sat on a bleak, damp October day. He was eager to see Sam Houston again, but he did not expect the President to spend much time with him. A Chief Executive, busy with all the problems of organizing a new government, did not have time to visit with the sons of old friends.

Sam Houston, President of Texas! Though too young to vote, Jack had campaigned actively for his fellow Tennessean before the election. But he could have saved his energies; Houston had been an overwhelming choice. Now, thought Jack proudly, shifting his weight in the uncomfortable chair, his part of Tennessee had produced two Presidents, Andrew Jackson and Sam Houston. The chair creaked and he had to smile as he mentally contrasted the offices of the Texas executive with the luxurious interior of "The Hermitage." His uncle Andrew had always received callers in his library—a room with high ceilings, mahogany wall-boarding, and a thick, dark-colored carpet. Here ceiling, walls, and floor were of rough, unpainted pine boards.

But there had been a humble beginning in Tennessee too, mused Jack. His grandfather, Robert Hays, one of the first settlers, had helped to shape the destiny of what was now the state of Tennessee. Perhaps another Hays would have a part in the development of the new country of Texas. In the five months since San Jacinto, the population of Texas had doubled. Most of the newcomers were land-breakers, home-builders. So far Jack had played only a small part, but if Sam Houston could build a great nation here, Jack would do what he could to help. In that way he could support himself in the meantime. He had received only one month's pay since his enlistment.

The secretary broke into Jack's thoughts, announcing, "The President will see you now."

A few seconds later Jack was warmly shaking hands with Sam Houston.

The President towered over his young visitor by several inches. Houston had changed little, Jack noticed, since the days when he was the outstanding political figure in Tennessee. His bright, deep-set eyes, the brightest Jack had ever seen, remained his outstanding feature.

"I wouldn't have known you," Houston declared. "But then you were only a little tyke when I saw you last. And now . . . a volunteer in our Texas army. I find that hard to believe."

"I'm old enough," Jack said with a smile. "It has been nine years, sir, since you saw me. I've grown up some, though not enough."

"You could stand some heft," agreed the President, "although I suppose that is not absolutely necessary. I've watched a bee chase a stout yearling all over a forty-acre pasture. Sit down, lad, and tell me all the news of your family and of Tennessee. I'm eager to learn every bit of it."

After unexpectedly resigning the governorship of Tennessee in 1827, Sam Houston had gone to live with the Cherokee Indians west of the Ozarks and had not returned to his native state. Jack briefly recounted the tragedies in his family. Houston voiced regret over the death of his parents.

"My uncle," explained Jack, "wanted to help me get started in business. But being a storekeeper didn't appeal to me. I reckon I'm too much for the outdoors. You should appreciate how I feel, sir," he added with a smile.

Sam Houston's eyes twinkled. Well should he appreciate such a spirit, and did. He had helped school the young son of Harmon Hays in Indian lore.

The President's curiosity seemed insatiable. Jack talked until he was almost exhausted. Finally Houston took pity on him, and on the visitors waiting outside.

"We've talked enough," he said regretfully. "It has been wonderful to visit with you. You have brought back a host of memories—some pleasant and some sad—but most of them pleasant."

Jack could guess what the unhappy recollections were. This broad-shouldered giant of a man had walked away from the governor's mansion and his bride without a word of explanation. For some mysterious reason, still not explained, Sam Houston had abruptly abandoned his brilliant career and begun life anew in the unsettled West among semi-civilized Indians. Just as dramatically, Houston's star had turned off from its setting course only to rise higher than ever. Certainly at this hour there was no more prominent man on the North American continent than Sam Houston.

As Jack turned to leave, the President stopped him. "We have not yet finished, my young friend. What can Houston do for you?" he asked.

Jack hesitated, then stammered, "Why, nothing, sir."

The President chuckled. "Oh, you're your father's son, all right. And your uncle's nephew. Are you assigned to service at present?"

"No, sir."

"You would like to be?"

Jack nodded. "Texas is my adopted country, sir. I want to be of service. If I'm not needed in the army, I propose to start surveying again. With the land opening up, there is bound to be a need for surveyors."

"There is," Houston agreed. "There is a need also, a dire need, for stouthearted men who will stand by Texas during the next few years. We have won our freedom apparently, but we face a time of crisis. Will we survive as an independent nation? Will we throw away what we have won in chaos and anarchy? What would you say, young sir, is the future of Texas?"

Jack licked his lips. How should he answer that?

"Speak up," commanded the President. "I will value your honest answer."

"Well, sir," the youth answered reluctantly, "there are those who think—who hope—that you will guide us into the Union. They think—they believe—that you came to Texas for that reason, and that you came with Uncle Andrew's blessing. They think that both of you—you and Uncle Andrew—are just waiting for the right time to bring Texas into the Union."

"Is that what you believe?" Houston asked crisply.

"I wouldn't say I *believe* it," Jack answered. "I will say that I *hope* it is true and that it happens that way."

Sam Houston studied the young man's face and his eyes grew even brighter. "You have a most direct manner," he murmured.

"I'm sorry, sir," Jack said quickly. "But you asked——"

"Don't apologize," the President broke in. "It is a highly commendable quality. Such a virtue should be nourished, not regretted. I wish I could reply as openly. I cannot. I cannot even tell you what I would do if it were in my power to shape our destiny. But I *can* promise you this, young man—and the more times this promise is quoted, the better. Houston is now of Texas, and of no other country. Whatever he does or causes to be done, it will be in good faith with the men who stood with him at San Jacinto. I hope you will be one of those who hold fast to that conviction in the next few years. I hope you will stand firmly beside me until Texas either is secure in her independence or has of her own choice merged herself with the American Union."

"That I'll do, sir," Jack promised. "Never doubt it."

"Excellent," said Houston with a nod, flashing his magnetic smile. "I had counted on you. Now about an assignment for you. You know, of course, that Mexico has repudiated the treaty that Santa Anna signed after San Jacinto?"

"Yes, sir."

"Their new administration has announced its intention to subdue Texas. I do not expect an immediate invasion, but we must take some precautions. I have ordered "Deaf" Smith's scouts to patrol the country south of San Antonio. With Deaf, I think, is the place for you. Texas needs fine, brave young men. I do. Give me enough such men, and I can defend my country against any danger."

Jack's eyes lighted up. He had heard many tales of Deaf Smith, the wary, competent scout and the President's most trusted lieutenant.

"I'd like that, sir," he said with more calmness than he felt.

"Then report to him at once. And let me hear from you again."

"I will, sir, and thank you."

Often in the next few days Jack thought back to that conversation. Houston was clever, all right. Skillfully he had led him to promise to follow faithfully whichever path Texas might take—as an independent nation or into the Union. Houston had obtained the commitment without revealing the slightest hint of his own preference. But his promise, mused Jack, was nothing to regret. Sam Houston was an easy man to believe in, and to follow.

So was Erastus "Deaf" Smith. No man knew Texas better, and the young recruit eagerly absorbed knowledge about the new country. Smith had immigrated to San Antonio in 1821. Poor health had forced him out of business. Believing outdoor life would cure him, he had taken to roaming the nearby hills. He had recovered his health, but not his hearing. During the revolution Sam Houston had sent him through the Mexican lines to learn the facts of the Alamo's fall.

Deaf Smith's company kept no regular formation; nor did they wear uniforms. Each man supplied his own clothes, horses, and weapons. Powder and ball were issued, but nothing else.

And their leader did not believe in long discussions about strategy or plans of operation. The thing to do, Jack Hays had quickly learned, was to follow without asking questions. If Captain Smith made or changed their plans in the saddle, that was "no skin off their noses." They had signed up to ride with him and that was what they did.

On March 3, 1837 the company left San Antonio, each man carrying a Mexican blanket behind his saddle. A small wallet held his salt, ammunition and *panolà*, parched corn, spiced and sweetened. They rode southward at a careful pace which immediately aroused the suspicions of the men. Smith held his dun mustang to a swinging walk for hour after hour: this gait, mused Jack, indicated a long march. Where to? There was no American settlement south of San Antonio de Bexar. The nearest town of any consequence in that direction was Laredo. And Laredo was in Mexico.

Jack's eyes gleamed. A march beyond the Nueces River could represent an important move on the part of the new nation. The Nueces wound through the rugged terrain south and east of the American settlements. Under Spanish and Mexican rule, the stream had marked the southern limits of the province known as Texas. The territory between the Nueces and the Rio Grande had been considered a part of Tamaulipas. But some Texas statesman, made bold by these long months of Mexican inactivity, was clamoring for the Lone Star Republic to establish the Rio Grande as its southern boundary. The Lone Star nation—so Texans loved to refer to their country. Theirs was a flag with a single big white star against a blue background.

Was that their purpose—the official sign that Texas claimed the area between the two rivers? Jack chuckled. If so, then theirs was a bold gesture indeed. Twenty men riding in open daylight to proclaim sovereignty over an area bigger than all of Tennessee and Kentucky combined! Nobody knew exactly how big it was, for no white man had ever traced the full course of the Rio Grande—at least none who had drawn maps or kept records. If the Rio Grande was the Texas boundary, then the Lone Star domain spread westward to the great desert and northward to the great snow-covered mountains. And what a heap of country lay in between!

In early afternoon they watered their horses in the Nueces and splashed on across the shallow stream.

"Well, we're in Mex country," announced Sam Walker with a grin. "Let's see what they aim to do about it."

Chapman Woolfork pointed to a giant rattlesnake slithering out of their path.

"That critter'd do plenty," he drawled, "if we'd climb down and fight his style."

"There's more of 'em in this country than you can shake a stick at," said William Powell, spitting amber tobacco juice toward the reptile to show his disgust. "I've been in this brush country before. Everything in it has fangs or thorns. It's the sorriest country you ever laid eyes on. There ain't gonna be no big fuss over who owns it. Mexicans ain't that stupid. They wouldn't even settle in this country when there wasn't nobody to stop 'em."

Powell spoke with some logic. As vast as this disputed area was, it did not contain a single Mexican settlement of any size, unless one included Santa Fe, nearly a thousand miles west of San Antonio. By mid-afternoon Deaf Smith's company had covered seventy or eighty miles and had seen not a single human habitation.

It was new country to twenty-year-old Jack Hays, and he studied it curiously. He edged his chestnut over to ride alongside Powell and learn the names of the bushes and the various types of cactus. Mesquite, *huisache, cenizo,* catclaw, *huajillo*—nearly all of this plant growth was new to him. The hilly region around San Antonio displayed an entirely different kind of plant life. Rugged slopes grew thick with small, gnarled varieties of oak and cedar, while mesquite and buffalo grass covered the valleys and plains. This land south of the Nueces stretched flat and monotonous. A surveyor, thought Jack, could mark off tracts almost as rapidly as his horse could walk. The biggest problem would be to establish a starting point.

All day Deaf Smith and his men rode steadily southward, and by nightfall they felt excitement anew. The Nueces was already a smart piece behind them! What was the wrinkle-faced old coot up to? If he aimed to take them all the way to the Rio Grande, then why didn't he let a body know!

He revealed his plans after they had made camp for the night.

Their destination was Laredo. He meant to raise the Texas flag on the church spire in that Mexican town on the anniversary of the fall of the Alamo!

Sam Walker's whoop greeted this explanation, and several other yells sounded almost as quickly. Only three days before, Smith's company had grumbled at their assignment to collect human bones lying about the old mission in San Antonio and give these gruesome remains some sort of decent burial. Jack himself had done more complaining about those orders than about any others he'd received since enlisting.

"I came to Texas to fight Mexicans," he told Sam Walker, "and so far about all I've done is help bury skeletons."

Deaf Smith had overhead that complaint. The captain reminded Jack of it as they munched their jerky and *panolà*.

"Tomorrow, bucko," Smith promised, "maybe you can put your itchy trigger finger to work."

"You think there'll be some shooting?" Woolfork asked eagerly.

"There's a garrison in Laredo," Smith said drily. "I don't look for 'em to roll over and play dead."

Woolfork grinned at Jack. "You gonna scalp the first Mex you kill, young 'un?" he asked.

"You can't scalp a Mexican," Powell told him. "Too easy. The coyotes wouldn't even eat the dead ones at San Jacinto. Too much pepper."

Jack smiled. The joshing and playfulness of these resourceful, hardy men had strained his patience at first. He liked them, respected their abilities, and intended to get along with them. But still he felt himself apart from them. For one thing, he was the youngest man in the company. Also, he clung to habits that brought him ridicule. In spite of their constant travel, Jack kept himself freshly shaved and presentable in appearance. Nor did he discard his Tennessee background and education to adopt the colorful speech of his companions. Much as he found to admire in the men of this company, he did not intend to take any of them as a pattern—not even Deaf Smith. He had other patterns to remember: Uncle Andrew and Sam Houston.

With daylight they were moving again. By noon they

sighted Chacon, a small Mexican settlement within ten miles of Laredo. Deaf Smith signaled for them to advance cautiously.

They lost sight of the adobe huts as the trail led through a *huisache* thicket. Smith reined up in the bright green shade.

"Two men," he ordered tersely, "go ahead and see what's waiting for us."

Jack spurred forward, and Deaf Smith's eyes twinkled.

"Sure, young 'un," he agreed. "You and Chap there."

Hays and Woolfork went toward the village at a brisk trot. They were within a hundred yards of the houses when the Mexican cavalry troop swept out from behind an adobe structure. Jack took one look at their shimmering lances and bright uniforms, then whirled his chestnut around. Woolfork reacted as quickly.

Both of them shot back at the Mexicans as they galloped off. They could not hit at that distance, especially not on a moving horse, but they meant to warn their companions what was ahead.

Nor did they flee directly back to the *huisache* grove. Jack and Woolfork veered off on a side trail, drawing the lancers after them, letting Smith's company pick its cover, be fully ready. If the Mexicans were foolish enough to chase hard after two invaders, they would get a rude shock when they had been maneuvered within range of the men hiding in the grove.

The lancers, some forty in number, seemed determined to ride the pair down. Jack and Woolfork could have outdistanced the company, but neither wanted that. Baiting the Mexicans, they allowed their pursuers to pull closer. Eager, dark-faced men were already shouting cries of triumph when the first fire came from the thicket.

Three or four brightly uniformed lancers tottered out of their saddles; the others stopped dead in their tracks. With shrill yells Jack and Woolfork joined their mates.

Quickly the lancers retreated out of range and then clustered close together for a council. Apparently they decided to surround the clump of *huisache*, for their ranks spread wide.

"Bold cusses," grunted Powell. "Ain't got us but two to one, and they aim to make a fight of it."

This remark was made in no spirit of braggadocio. Smith's Texans honestly felt that they had the edge in any such skirmish. Forty to twenty, the Texans behind cover, their hunting rifles against Mexican *escopetas* . . . Jim Dunn summed up their attitude—this kind of shooting was duck soup.

The lancers spread into a circle, then sent one unit charging head-on. The Texans broke up that sally with a volley that claimed three more victims. Two lancers lost control of their horses and could not turn back when their leader ordered a retreat. The pair stormed into the thicket and were quickly made prisoners.

Another vain charge, and the lancers withdrew. The Texans came out of the thicket and reckoned their toll. Ten Mexicans were dead and at least that many had suffered wounds. In addition to their prisoners, Deaf Smith's men had captured twenty horses, an extra mount for each of them.

The damage to the Texans totaled four flesh wounds. Dunn had a ball in his shoulder, the nearest thing to a casualty.

"The young 'un led 'em right to our blind," said Powell gloatingly. "It was just like shooting geese on a pond."

Excited over their victory, the men wanted to push on

and capture the village itself, but Deaf Smith would not agree. For the first time he told them something of his orders. This foray was supposed to be a challenge, nothing more. His instructions were to fall back when he encountered strong opposition. What he needed now was information about enemy strength in Laredo. Several of the men asked for the assignment of making the lone ride to the Mexican town, but Smith chose Jack.

"Can't tell about some of you jaybirds," drawled the scout. "You might get sidetracked by *señoritas* or tequila. Bucko there will tend to business." And he ordered the others back into camp.

Jack rode a wide circle around Chacon and to the limits of Laredo. The size of the town surprised him; he had not expected to find it inhabited by several hundred people. The strength of the garrison, too, was quickly apparent. He reported back to Deaf Smith that Laredo was defended by at least a hundred soldiers.

"Too many for us to take on," Deaf decided regretfully. "Let's mosey on back to San Antonio."

Grumblingly the men obeyed. They camped the next night on the Frio River, less than a half-day's ride from San Antonio. Dunn's wound appeared to be healing; he would have a scar to show for this bold jaunt and nothing else.

"I figger," Deaf Smith confided to Jack before they reached San Antonio, "that now they'll take some notice of us in the capital. I aim to ask old Sam for men and any extra guns he can hustle up."

"Old Sam" was President Houston, of course. Many Texans called him that in affection and awe. Others used the nickname in derision.

"And I aim to recommend appointment of a sergeant,"

Smith went on, speaking to the whole group. "I figger on nominating Jack there. Anybody got any objections?"

The embarrassed youth would not look at the men, but kept his eyes lowered. He need not have been either embarrassed or doubtful of the reaction of his companions. Not one voiced a protest.

3

The Texas Rangers—
and Captain Jack Hays

A full-fledged sergeant! Jack carefully penned a letter to his younger brother and sister. He wanted them to know of his promotion and of the bold raid into enemy territory. But he also wanted them to know the truth about his circumstances. He was far from being ready to have them join him. He explained:

We are a strange sort of company. Our main duty is to watch for any attack from Mexico. It's been fifteen months since the battle of San Jacinto but no sign of another Mexican invasion yet. We ride some patrols along the two roads leading into San Antonio, but the only Mexicans we encounter are *banditos*, not regular soldiers. The rest of the time we are in our camp on the Medina River or in San Antonio. Every week or so some of us go hunting for wild cattle or mustangs. We must furnish our own rations and since we haven't been paid but once this summer, we depend on wild beef and game for food. We spend some of our leisure time curing hides. Most of my fellow soldiers are wearing buckskin and I'll probably be doing the same before long. My clothes are nearly threadbare

41

and I have very little money left. With the Republic
of Texas so destitute, there's little chance that we'll be
paid soon. We are greatly discouraged about our
chances of annexation into the Union. We never expected that this would become a political issue in the
United States.

Back came an answer—not immediately, for mail exchange between the Republic of Texas and the United
States was slow and irregular. His brother and sister wrote
briefly of their activities, including their plans for school
that autumn. Mr. Cage sent a long missive, treating mostly
the sentiment in the United States toward accepting Texas
into the Union. The South, he stated, mostly favored it,
but Whig leaders from the Northern states held the upper
hand in Congress. And the Whigs meant to oppose the
annexation of any more slave-holding territory. Annexation,
wrote Mr. Cage, was a long way off. Courteously, but with
his usual stiffness, he offered assistance if and when Jack
decided to return to his native country.

Jack smiled. How little his uncle knew about him! Or
about the other migrants from the United States who kept
swelling the Texas population. Such discouraging reports
from across the Sabine River only strengthened a Texas
political faction, which had Mirabeau B. Lamar as a cham-
pion. These Texans wanted to build the Lone Star nation
greater, not continue suit for admission as a state. But,
whatever Texas' political future, Jack had no intention of
returning to Mississippi. He had just sipped the wonders
of this new frontier. His thirst wasn't satisfied by any
means.

Not even the friction within the scout company damp-
ened his spirits. Deaf Smith retired from military service
in that summer of 1837 because of failing health. Colonel

Henry W. Karnes, his successor, was a fearless soldier but no cavalry scout. Nor was he the sort to get along with the free-spirited men who had served Smith so well.

Karnes believed in regular military discipline, which went "against the grain" of these rugged individualists.

"Where does he get off acting like a regular officer?" demanded Powell. "Him and his drilling and his notions about saluting. If I hankered to be a sure-enough soldier, I'd sure pick an army with regular paydays."

"That goes for me too," said Woolfork. "Much more of this and I'm lighting out of here."

Jack's feelings were divided. Since each man furnished his own horse, weapons, and regalia, their unimpressive appearance couldn't be helped. But would it hurt them to drill occasionally and hold ranks when they rode on maneuvers?

Woolfork grinned. That's what came of making a button sergeant, he said. But those grizzled scouts didn't resent Jack's reproofs. They had liked him from the start, and that feeling increased when he wangled permission from Colonel Karnes to employ them on surveying jobs.

"They need the money," he insisted when Karnes demurred. "So do I. These new settlers must have their lands surveyed. We can help them get located and earn a few dollars ourselves without neglecting our duties.

The colonel finally consented, and Jack got his license as a deputy surveyor of Bexar County. He took Woolfork and Powell to mark off a tract on the San Marcos River. They fought off an Indian party and then ran their lines. Returning to San Antonio, Jack found a dozen landowners waiting to engage him. Most surveyors balked at assignments in the unfriendly hill country. They could not find helpers on short notice who were crack shots and willing to face

Indian warriors. Jack and his team worked steadily through September and October. By November he could afford homespun clothes, two extra horses, and another brace of pistols; and most of Karnes' scouts had earned money that autumn to replenish their powder and lead.

It was well they did, for a changing administration meant a change in Indian policy.

The Republic of Texas had modeled its government after the United States, but with some exceptions. The President was elected for a three-year term, for instance, and could not succeed himself. Sam Houston, then, though still the strong man of the nation, was bowing out of office.

A sergeant with Karnes did not worry too much about the election. Three candidates were announced for that office—Mirabeau B. Lamar, James Collingsworth, and Peter W. Grayson.

Jack had no personal preference. Collingsworth was from Tennessee too, but Lamar had helped win the victory at San Jacinto. The only disturbing thing about Lamar's speeches was his apparent ambition for Texas to remain a separate nation. "We don't need to sue further for annexation into the Union," declared Lamar. "We can build Texas into a stronger country than even our mother land. What's to prevent us from extending the Lone Star borders all the way to the Pacific Ocean!"

Talk of westward expansion stirred Jack, of course, as it had his father and grandfather and Andrew Jackson. But the sergeant nourished the hope that Texas would continue its efforts to join the Union.

There was no telling how the three-way election might have turned out, for it was never held. Personal tragedies overcame both Grayson and Collingsworth during the campaign and both committed suicide. Lamar became President by default, and immediately announced an aggressive policy against all Indian tribes. A volunteer force marched into north Texas to expel the Cherokees. That campaign was easy to win, but Lamar's policy aroused a new savage foe— the Comanches. These red men swept out of the prairies and raided the full width of the Texas Republic, reaching Linnville on the Gulf Coast. Colonel Karnes was ordered to drive the Comanches out of their winter hunting grounds along the Pedernales River.

The scouts were taking the field against a nomadic Indian tribe! "We're in for it," predicted Ben McCulloch, one of the new recruits. He had skirmished against the Comanches north of the Red River and knew what the company faced. "You can't fight them red devils. They won't stay put."

"Injuns are Injuns," grunted Sam Walker. "There's a way to fight 'em. You just have to outsmart 'em." He had helped subdue the Creeks in Alabama, and his companions listened to him respectfully, especially Sergeant Hays.

The scouts trailed along behind Colonel Karnes as they followed Arroyo Seco into the granite-strewn hills west of San Antonio. The colonel had gotten nowhere with his ideas of a regular formation, but these twenty frontiersmen quickly obeyed his orders to take cover. They crouched in a chaparral thicket while down upon them thundered two hundred half-naked Indians.

They were Comanches, all right. Ben McCulloch pointed to the pennant flying from their leader's lance. That was the *Oo-len-ten-to-ka*, he said, their war emblem. Jack crouched next to McCulloch and fingered his trigger. This was a new style of Indian attack! The Comanches circled around the thicket, coming closer and closer. Suddenly the party veered and attacked the white men in a headlong rush.

Karnes proved a cool commander. His scouts held their fire until the menacing riders came within a hundred yards. Then the Texans shot carefully, reloading as rapidly as they could. The Comanche charge wavered, but the red men hurriedly reformed their circle after falling back to a safe distance.

Hundreds of arrows had rained into the thicket with no loss of human life. But the chaparral was not thick enough to shelter the company's horses too, and the scouts lost more mounts as the second murderous Comanche assault came swiftly. This time the Indians brought their circling maneuver to within seventy yards.

There was no breaking up their formation either. These prairie nomads offered no targets. They could fire their arrows under the bellies of their galloping ponies. Any shot fired at them was so much wasted lead. It was easy to see that they wanted to draw the white man's fire, then attack before the men in the thicket could reload. But Jack and his companions knew better than to make that mistake; the fusillade, ready when the Comanches struck, staggered them. The assailants fell back, leaving ten or twelve more dead warriors. A third assault was also repulsed, and this time the red men abandoned the field. Twenty savages were killed, as many others wounded. The scouts had one dead and three wounded.

But Sergeant Hays quickly realized why the white men could not consider this a victory. They had lost every one of their horses. They had no choice but to limp back to San Antonio and mark time until they had managed to get new mounts.

It was a hollow victory indeed. Every mile they walked,

carrying their saddles and other gear, added to their disgust.

"It's just like I told you," McCulloch told Walker. "You chase 'em off and what have you done? You've killed some but not enough. They go gallivanting off to hit again."

"They're boogers, all right." admitted Sam. "The Creeks—you could corner 'em for a fight." He gestured toward the open prairie. "Reckon there's no cornering anything in this country."

"Not a Comanche," Ben said. "They can outride us."

Jack was listening attentively. Walker and McCulloch, he decided, were a cut above the average frontiersman. As he struggled along with his heavy saddle, Jack reviewed what he knew about them. Ben was a native of west Tennessee, a boyhood friend of Davey Crockett. Walker had come originally from Maryland but had fought and trapped over most of the South.

The Comanches could outmaneuver them on horseback! Sergeant Hays brooded over that as the weary company trudged on. It was true. These prairie Indians rode their shaggy ponies as well as Mexican *charros*. Their mounts were superior to the white man's too. Jack Hays, born and raised in the tradition of thoroughbred stock, did not like to admit that. But it must be faced. The native mustang was superior to the thoroughbred in this rugged terrain. The mustang was hardier and more agile. Probably more tireless, too, with its lope and easier gait for both horse and rider once a man was accustomed to it. Jack sighed, remembering his boyhood pride in his stiff, erect posture in the saddle. He'd have to scrap all he had been taught. He must even get a new saddle, a high-horned one.

For the usual adage about Indians had to be rephrased to fit this open country. In the South they had said that to catch an Indian, you had to think like one. But before you could catch a Comanche, you had to outride him.

But Colonel Karnes was not convinced. He counted off the warlike tribes that had been subdued by dogged infantry pursuit. The white man's superiority, he insisted, was due to his better military organization. He wangled funds out of the War Department and regrouped his scouts for another assault on the Comanches.

This time he had sixty followers. The number made no difference to the hard-riding savages. The Comanches hurled a pincer-like formation against Karnes' force. The white men dismounted and formed their usual circle; arrows rained down upon the besieged scouts. Again Karnes managed to lead most of his company back to San Antonio, but at the loss of their horses and scant supplies. His funds spent, Karnes ordered his men into winter camp and took a leave of duty himself.

Jack knew that this meant the breakup of Deaf Smith's old company. The scouts couldn't keep themselves available for immediate duty. San Antonio offered no employment for such men. Jack chose a picked few to help him with surveys, and the others scattered in all directions.

He worked feverishly through the Christmas season. By the end of 1838 he had surveyed sixty-eight tracts in the San Antonio vicinity. But, as he ruefully wrote his relatives, he had accumulated little money.

I seldom get all my fees in cash [he explained]. To get business I have to take land certificates in partial payment. I suppose I will realize something from these certificates eventually, but now they have no cash value. There is little left after I have paid my crew. We never get any official communication from the

nning his recommendations as well. He had
ite ideas, he said boldly, on the organization of
ompany. He hoped the President would not
n presumptuous, but he felt obliged to offer
stions.

nt to deliver the report himself, but Samuel A.
tervened. Maverick was a prominent citizen of
io, its leading spokesman except for the con-
ayor, Juan Seguin.

read Jack's recommendations carefully, sug-
hange or two to give the report more dignity.
wyer offered to present the recommendations to
amar himself.

rman of a committee of citizens formed to de-
Antonio," he explained, "I am entitled to a
fore any congressional committee. Let me do the
ack. That's my profession."

k returned a week later with a bulky package
ecretary of War. The envelope contained a draft
Republic's treasury, a letter of commendation
ar himself, and authorization from Congress for
ee Hays to organize and serve as captain of a
of "Texas Rangers."

lid you manage it?" asked Jack.

uble," smiled Maverick. "President Lamar asked
for funds to organize frontier defense. He didn't
Sam Houston headed the opposition and he still
big stick in this country. Sam's followers voted
ry appropriation except yours. Sam said that you
ily officer Lamar has who's worth his salt. So you
ointed in a hurry."

ook his head. He didn't relish being the topic of

Adjutant General, so I'm not sure about my military
status. Maybe I am still a soldier, maybe not.

He did not disclose his dream to his Mississippi kin:
these assistants would be the nucleus of the new company
he intended to organize. This troop would serve not only
as frontier scouts but as a mobile fighting force.

The men scorned regular drills, but they learned more
about their future work all the time. Jack challenged them
to match the horsemanship of Mexican *charros*. They
traded their English saddles for the high-horned Mexican
variety. They performed daredevil stunts while riding mustangs at top speed. They acquired pistol marksmanship
from atop a galloping horse.

Nor did the young organizer have to wait long for the
chance to prove his troop's merit.

In January, 1839, President Lamar sent a courier to San
Antonio. A rumor had reached the Chief Executive that a
Mexican invasion was forming at Laredo. The courier
brought orders for Colonel Karnes and the scout company
to investigate at once.

The courier was amazed at what Jack told him. No scout
company active on the frontier! How long had this been
true? Since early December, Jack answered.

Couldn't the sergeant do something? Jack nodded. He
could lead his personal retinue south and investigate the
rumor. Did he have President Lamar's sanction to act as a
volunteer captain?

Lordee, yes, promised the relieved courier. Anything, just
go. Jack's eyes twinkled as he led thirteen horsemen along
the *camino real*. He had been sure that just such an opportunity would arise. If the troop could acquit itself well in
this emergency, he would have cause to report personally

to President Lamar. Maybe, he mused, the formal organization of his company could come sooner than he had expected.

The troop traveled over a hundred miles without incident. The Texans drove off one *bandito* force but encountered no other opposition until they neared Laredo.

Suddenly a bend in the *real* revealed an advancing Mexican troop. The dragoons halted when they saw the Texans. A lone rider came forward, signaling for a parley.

Jack responded immediately. The Mexican turned out to be Laredo's *alcalde*. Scouts, he said, had reported the approaching Texans. The *alcalde* pointed back to the smartly uniformed dragoons. The Texans were outnumbered almost four to one. Did the young *capitán* wish to surrender before his force was annihilated?

Jack shook his head. He had come to test the strength of Laredo's defenses, he said calmly. He added that his instructions were to capture the town if he met resistance.

The *alcalde* sputtered. Such insolence, such braggadocio! He was waving the dragoons forward before he rejoined them.

Jack's nondescript-looking troopers chuckled as he described the interview. "Well," said McCulloch, "we might just capture the town at that. Meanwhile, we'll lick these fancy dragoons for sure."

The lancers came on cautiously. Their volley from a hundred yards away did no damage at all to the Texans.

"They'll have to get closer than that," grinned Sam. "Those *escopetas* aren't the guns for long-range shooting."

The Texans used their rifles as the dragoons threatened a charge. Their weapons were superior to Mexican carbines, which had such a heavy recoil that a good "bead" was im-

---

possible. One horse wounded.

But such long-range s Jack gathered his follow

"Wait until their nex them."

The dragoons had to clumsy *escopetas*. They the ground to aim at the

"Charge," Jack yelled over his mustang's neck l over their heads as they Mexicans. Texan pistols s could remount. Jack shot

The dragoons fled or t loping these Texans, whos chargers. The troop circlec rushed into them pell-mel lance, and Jack's men carri quickly surrendered; eight wounded.

Jack dismounted and o ward. How many troops w moaned that worthy. The whole garrison. He begged

Jack nodded, convinced was not part of his instr President Lamar feared tha izing at Laredo. It wasn't. sponsibility as a volunteer.

He ordered the prisoners cross the Rio Grande. Then back to San Antonio and wr

---

carefully p formed def a frontier consider h these sugg

Jack me Maverick i San Anton troversial i

Maveric gesting a Then the President

"As cha fend San hearing be debating,

Maveri from the upon the from Lan John Co company

"How

"No t Congress get them swings tl down ev are the c were app

Jack s

congressional debate. He was just grateful that his recommendations had been approved without opposition.

Samuel Maverick held out his hand. "Let me be the first to officially congratulate Captain Jack Hays of the Texas Rangers," he said gravely.

4

Jack Finds a New Ally

The stir over the Laredo skirmish surprised Jack. Newspapers in Houston and Columbia praised the maneuver as the "boldest blow struck for Texas since San Jacinto." Several congressmen made speeches declaring that such captains as the "gallant Hays" would prove the Republic's stature as an independent nation. His Rangers, reading the plaudits, wondered what the fuss was all about.

"Shucks," scoffed Walker, "we didn't cut a caper as all that. I've been in hotter fights and never mentioned it."

Jack nodded. They had disproved an invasion rumor and surprised a small Mexican force with their sudden rush. But it had not been a major victory and he certainly did not claim the organization of his Ranger company as a "milestone in Texas history." Nor did he like the references to himself as the "boy captain." He had turned twenty-one. What did he have to do to prove his maturity?

Mr. Maverick interpreted the sudden interest in young Captain Hays.

"We are desperate for something to boast about," explained the lawyer. "Texas is trying to establish credit and get official recognition in Europe. The general feeling in London and Paris is that we couldn't defend ourselves

54

against a strong invading force. Such exploits as yours refute that. The United States newspapers have printed accounts of your raid too. Southern journalists seize every opportunity to glamorize Texas figures. You can understand why."

Jack nodded: the Southern states wanted Texas in the Union. He didn't voice his own feelings. Annexation was a controversial topic in Texas as well as in Washington. A good soldier never became identified with any political faction. But the son of Harmon Hays and the nephew of Andrew Jackson was not neutral. He'd led a flag West— the same flag as his fathers.

"Well," Jack said slowly, "our little dido wasn't much to crow about. The big thing is getting money for our company. Now maybe we can do something about the Comanches. They're the boogers, Mr. Maverick."

The lawyer nodded. He had driven out to the Ranger camp in his buggy. It was his first glimpse of the scout headquarters, and he could not help but chuckle as he looked around him. There was nothing but a grove of trees to provide partial shelter for twenty-odd men and their horses. Captain John Coffee Hays, the center of such wide attention, had only a brush lean-to. In plain homespun, with no evidence of military status, Jack squatted on his haunches like an Indian.

"Yes," agreed Mr. Maverick, "the Comanches are our most pressing problem. Congress can get stirred up about a raid against Mexico, but not a chase along the Pedernales. That's the main business of our citizens' committee, Captain. We want the region around San Antonio settled. We'll never build up our trade until it is. We'll cooperate with your company one hundred per cent. We'll send delegates to Congress any time your appropriation is threatened."

"That'd be a great help," answered Jack. "It's not easy to keep men in camp when they're not getting paid."

"Every member of our committee appreciates how you have done that," Maverick said heartily. "We know that you personally have kept a nucleus of fighting men together. We want Congress and the whole nation to know it too." His eyes twinkled. "We have planned a little ball and reception for you and your men, Captain. It won't be much of an occasion, but at least it will show our appreciation."

"Oh, that isn't necessary," Jack said quickly. "If we can just depend on your help with Congress . . ."

"That's part of our plan," the lawyer interrupted. "We have invited President Lamar and his staff to attend. He rather surprised us by his quick acceptance. May we count on your attendance, Captain?"

Jack sighed. He saw no way out of accepting.

"And your men too," added Mr. Maverick.

Jack hesitated. His rough-riders at a formal ball! The other man guessed his thoughts. "The ladies insist on that," he explained. "Mrs. W. I. Riddle, who is in charge of the guest list, feels that the ball won't be a success unless every man in your company is present."

"I'll put it to them," Jack told him, "but I can't guarantee they'll come." He shook his head and smiled. "They're an independent bunch, Mr. Maverick. They do pretty much as they please when we're not on duty."

The lawyer nodded. "I know. But try to persuade them to attend. I think it's important to the future of the Rangers, and of Texas."

Within twenty-four hours the members of Jack's company were accusing their commander of "double-crossing" them. He had told them it would be just a get-together, they grumbled; had said only a few San Antonio people would be present.

"Hellfire," snapped Walker, "the President is coming and the adjutant general and some congressmen—all the high monkey-monks. We signed up to fight, not dance quadrilles."

Jack let them protest. He was in the same boat, he said. He owned no dress clothes either. In three years he had bought no garments except those suited for hard wear in the saddle. The company had to make frantic arrangements. For instance, Jack himself would have to take turns wearing a coat with Mike Chevaille and John Howard.

A few nights later, in his borrowed finery, he stood in the receiving line to greet guests and then danced the first number. As soon as the music stopped, he slipped outside and Chevaille had his caper to the music. Then Howard got his turn.

Such an arrangement was bound to be noticed. The honor guest couldn't be absent from the floor two dances out of three without causing wonder. Mrs. Riddle, a persevering lady, soon guessed the reason. She whispered to Mrs. Maverick and that lady relayed the explanation to Mayor Seguin. The Rangers were missing out on a great share of the fun because they didn't have coats for every man.

Mayor Seguin promptly took off his own coat and quietly passed the word for others to do the same. President Lamar noticed the sudden predominance of shirt sleeves and asked the reason. The Chief Executive chuckled and removed his own frock coat. By midnight the Rangers felt at ease and were enjoying the ball.

Mirabeau B. Lamar was a handsome figure of a man, gracious of speech, burning with enthusiasm for his adopted

country. He listened intently as Jack described their difficulties with the Comanches. The President had been a
soldier too; at the Battle of San Jacinto he had won immediate recognition for his boldness.

"I understand your difficulty," said Lamar. "It's a far
cry from the way we were trained to fight east of the
Mississippi." He frowned thoughtfully. "Artillery would
accomplish nothing," he mused. "You couldn't haul can-
nons across the prairie and in and out of the hills. I think
you've hit the nail on the head, Captain. We must learn
to whip the Comanches at their own style of fighting."

The ball turned out to be a great success. Jack, rolling
into his blanket in the early hours of the morning, thought
back to his conversation with the President. He could not
deny that he had been quite impressed by Lamar's sincerity.
The Chief Executive honestly believed that Texas should
pursue its own destiny rather than join the Union. Were
his dreams too grandiose? Some Texans were charging so,
including Sam Houston. Jack turned over on his side with
a grunt. That wasn't for him to decide. He was a captain
and the President was his superior officer. The Rangers
already had more to worry about doing than they could
get done. Let others scan distant horizons and predict a
glorious future. Jack Hays had the responsibility of the
two *camino reals* leading up from the Rio Grande and the
wild Comanches. Either one would have been enough.

On a cold, drizzly day Jack settled himself in his lean-to
to write a lengthy letter to his brother and sister. He had
already informed them of his promotion and the formation
of a Ranger company based on his ideas. But this day, eyes
twinkling, a smile playing around the corners of his mouth,
he tried to describe some of his new additions.

Would they believe such characters as "Alligator" Davis and "Bull" Bateman? Jack doubted it, but did his best to describe the two men anyhow.

Davis was a lanky man, slow of speech and action. One afternoon he was lying in the shade, watching his captain test prospective recruits. The promise of regular pay had brought would-be volunteers flocking to the Medina camp. Jack devised his own tests for the applicants. One test required the applicant to hit a target while galloping past at full speed. Most of them couldn't and the young captain rejected those who didn't qualify. That particular afternoon none of six prospects pleased the leader.

Davis saw an alligator swimming in the river. "I'll pull that critter in for you, Cap," he offered. "He'll make us a good hand."

The lanky man plunged into the river. Locking grips with the monster, he was knocked backward and almost drowned by a blow from the alligator's tail. After more tussling the Ranger finally got astride the beast and caught a jaw with either hand. Slowly he forced the alligator into shallow water and toward the bank. At last he hauled his quarry onto dry ground.

"Here's a good one," he panted. "Won't be the ugliest *hombre* we got either. He's a lot better-looking than Big Foot there."

"Big Foot" Wallace was a giant, gaunt Virginian who insisted upon riding a mule instead of a mustang. No mustang could carry his weight all day, he claimed. Big Foot's stories were as endless and humorous as Alligator's.

Wallace had refused to attend the civic ball. He was "leary of females," he explained to Jack, not having recovered from an unhappy experience. He had been engaged to marry a young lady, only to have his hair fall out as the result of a sudden illness. Hearing that bear grease would restore his locks, Wallace retreated to a cave along the Colorado River and treated his scalp. A trusted friend was his only contact with the outside world during these weeks. In due time Big Foot's hair grew back—but the young woman had married another swain during his absence.

Simon Bateman was known as "Bull" after a comical experience with a shambling *ladino*. Bateman had sold a Mississippi plantation in order to move to Texas. He was one Ranger who had the financial means to acquire and develop a large tract of land, but he preferred this roving, adventurous life. He had challenged the bull just to show he was not afraid. The indignant bull had tossed him over a rail fence.

Except for Billy Anderson, there were only young men in Jack's reorganized company. Anderson was in his fifties, but still able to outride and outfight most of his younger contemporaries. He had been in Texas since the 1820's, and his bitter hatred of the Comanches dated back to the scalping of his older brother. Anderson particularly liked one-man patrols, for then he could "lift the hair" of his savage victims.

When he had too much to drink, Billy regaled his fellow Rangers with his yarns and his "snake performance." He kept a wiry rattler in a small cage. He would hold the snake in one hand and let the reptile strike at the muscular portion of his left arm. But he wouldn't touch his "pet" while sober. Whisky, he claimed, made him immune to the snake's poison.

Such stories, Jack knew, would fascinate Bobby and Susan.

He had almost finished the letter when a visitor arrived in a buggy. Jack folded his paper and stepped outside.

Sam Walker stood talking to a massive man with short, blond hair and a ruddy complexion.

"Jack, this is C. M. Swenson. Brought something for you."

Jack held out his hand to acknowledge Walker's terse introduction. "Yah," Swenson said cordially. "Captain Yack Hays. Glad to know you, Captain." He unwrapped a piece of oilskin and revealed two pistols. "President Lamar asked to bring you these. My compliments."

Jack's eyes gleamed with immediate interest. He handed one of the revolvers to Walker, studied the other. It was bigger than any pistol he had ever handled. And he immediately realized the utility of the revolving cylinder.

Swenson, a Swedish immigrant to Texas, explained about the guns in his broken English. He owned one general store near Columbia and meant to open another in one of the western settlements, probably Bastrop. He had just returned from a business trip to New York. While there he had heard reports of a repeating pistol that a young inventor named Samuel Colt was trying to sell in Washington and Europe. Swenson had brought a dozen of the guns to Texas. President Lamar had suggested that he present a brace of the weapons to Captain Hays.

"And I do," he said. "Yah. Who else puts guns to better use than Captain Yack Hays?"

Jack murmured his thanks. He twirled the weapon in a circle. He liked its feel, and yet he didn't. Swenson handed him several cartridges.

"Try it, yah," urged the Swedish merchant. "Shoots good."

Jack loaded the pistol, aimed at a nearby sapling. His features glowed as bark flew. Swiftly he pulled the trigger.

Bark flew again. Sam Walker loaded the other pistol and matched Jack's marksmanship.

"She's a doozie," declared Sam.

Swenson glowed his pleasure at their appreciation. He ate with the Rangers around their campfire and repeated what he knew about the repeating pistols. The man Colt had a small factory in New Jersey. He had manufactured some three or four hundred of the weapons, but had not found buyers for them. No government was interested. It was Swenson's impression that the inventor was bankrupt.

The Swedish merchant traveled on the next morning. Behind him, the Rangers squabbled over whose turn it was to experiment with the new weapons. They had shot up all their bullets in a day's time. But the pistols were not put away and forgotten. Sam and Jack brought out the weapons again and again to study and criticize.

"There oughta be a guard for the trigger," mused Sam, "so a man can wear it in his belt. And the butt oughta be heavier. Heavier hammer too—so if the trigger catches, a man can still get off his shot." He shook his shaggy head. "Maybe that's what we oughta do, Jack. Invent a pistol for a man on horseback. So you can throw lead at Comanches without having to drop down and form a circle."

Jack nodded. He had been thinking along the same lines. Repeating pistols that could be fired from the saddle of a galloping horse! Given such weapons, there was no limit to what his Rangers could accomplish against Indians or Mexicans.

The idea grew into an obsession. Making an abrupt decision, Jack left his troop in McCulloch's charge and rode to Washington-on-the-Brazos. An audience with President Lamar was easy to arrange. Nor was the Chief Executive slow to appreciate the young captain's ideas about the repeating pistol.

"They won't do for us like they are," Jack explained. "But surely the inventor can make the changes we want. If we could equip our cavalry with these pistols, sir . . ." He shook his head, unable to predict just how much his company would benefit.

Lamar quickly agreed that the Republic of Texas should contact the New York inventor.

"We have some funds," said the President. "Enough to experiment with the new weapons anyhow." His eyes reflected his rising enthusiasm. "We are a new nation," he said solemnly, "and I think it fitting that we be receptive to new ideas in armaments. Captain, I suggest that you travel to New York yourself and make arrangements with Mr. Colt to adapt these guns to our frontier use."

Jack hesitated. The inspiration was mostly Sam Walker's, he explained. He did not want to be put into the position of accepting the credit for an idea originated by a lieutenant.

"Very well," smiled Lamar, "we shall send Sam Walker. You are much too modest for your own good, my young sir. But no doubt that is why you get the loyalty of your soldiers. Will you instruct Walker to report to the Secretary of War as soon as possible?"

"Yes, sir," Jack said promptly. His eyes twinkled. "In the interests of international relations, sir," he said, "you had better warn New York City that Sam Walker is coming. I don't imagine they've seen anything like him up there."

The President chuckled. "You might advise Sam to leave his buckskins at home. Probably our cousins in the United

States wouldn't appreciate the odors of bear grease and camp smoke."

Jack hurried back to the Medina River camp. Twice his company had sallied out in pursuit of ravaging Comanches. Both times the Rangers had overtaken the red men and forced them into battle. Texan rifles had taken a toll of the prairie nomads too. Both war parties, however, had galloped off after realizing they could not wipe out the white soldiers.

Walker protested that he was not about to go to a place like New York City. He had seen a city once—Baltimore. He didn't like crowds and houses built smack up against each other. And he sure didn't like the idea of trusting himself to a pitching steamboat. What if the danged contraption sank!

He finally yielded. In new homespun shirt and trousers, and a borrowed dress coat and flowing tie, he rode toward the national capital. The terse word came back from Washington-on-the-Brazos: Sam had been issued his expense money and his authority from the Republic of Texas to buy adapted five-shooters.

Long weeks passed. Finally, one mid-afternoon, Walker returned to the Medina River camp. He'd never been through such an ordeal in his life, he declared. Just finding where that fellow Colt lived was enough to put a man in his grave. But finally he'd tracked the *hombre* down. Living in a basement, slowly starving to death. Couldn't sell his repeating pistols for sour apples. "You oughta seen his eyes light up when I told him who I was. The Republic of Texas —he had to think twice to realize what I was talking about. Then he warmed up. Caught on right quick to the changes we want. Said he'd designed his weapons for use by navies, not cavalry. Hadn't thought of horsemen using 'em. Said he'd get to work on the guns he had in stock. About three hundred of 'em. Said he'd add the trigger guards and give weight to the hammer and the pistol butts. Insisted I hang around until he'd worked over one pistol.

"It'll do the job for us, Jack. Colt promises to have us three hundred or more of those revolvers by Christmastime."

That was Sam's full account of his trip. Laconic—yes. But what else could be expected of Sam Walker? By the next day his trip was a sore subject with him. He took a certain amount of ribbing, then put his foot down. The next galoot to shoot off his mouth, he threatened, would get a dose of knuckles. He hadn't wanted to go in the first place; Jack had talked him into it. Now certain smart *hombres* had better attend to their own knitting or they'd have a man after them. Sam emphasized that word "man."

But, six weeks later, the veteran frontier fighter felt quite different. First he was startled to learn that a package for him had reached San Antonio. Big Foot Wallace denied any jocular intent. "It's at Mr. Maverick's office," said Big Foot. "He asked me to pass the word. It's no shenanigan."

And it wasn't. Walker rode into town, received the bulky package, and opened it suspiciously. He blinked at the contents, then . . .

"Never felt so much like bawling in my life," he confessed to Jack later. He had timidly called the captain out of the camp to show the package's content. He wanted Jack to see the pistols and read Samuel Colt's letter, then suggest how the other Rangers should be told about both.

The revolvers were exactly as Sam had proposed—except for one thing—a gleaming name-plate. It spelled out WALKER.

These, Sir [read Mr. Colt's accompany message], are the first four pistols re-designed according to your ideas. I am more than delighted with the revised product and expect to fill your Republic's order on schedule. But I wanted to send you these weapons as a small personal token of my appreciation. Yes, Sir, this is the Walker gun! I could do no less for the man who sought me out of oblivion and showed me what my pistol must do if it is to become a gun of destiny. I humbly ask that you present two of these weapons to your gallant young Captain, Jack Hays. I would like to boast that Sam Walker and Captain Hays wear the first Colt revolvers in the American West.

"It kinda gets me," Sam admitted as Jack handed back Colt's letter. "The best danged gun ever made, and it's named for me."

Jack and Sam tested the new guns in secrecy. Every detail was what they had expected, except for one very important item: How could a man wear two such heavy weapons in his regular belt?

"Lordee," brooded Sam. "You get your choice—tote these things around and you can't keep your breeches up."

The answer seemed a second belt, used only to support the two guns. Jack visited a Mexican harness-maker. Sí, said the native, he could make them heavy belts. But the Colts still hung down. Again the two puzzled men found the obvious answer. The leather expert was dubious. Pouches to let the pistols hang against their hips? He would try. The improvement was considerable, even if the finished product was not entirely satisfactory. Now, at least, they could wear the guns in the saddle without the steel barrels pressing into their ribs.

The pleased pair slipped away from camp to practice their marksmanship. When they were ready to show their skill, Jack called the entire company into camp. Then he and Sam rode off a hundred yards, whirled their mustangs around, and galloped back. None of the mystified Rangers saw either man raise a weapon, but suddenly a rain of lead tore into the cottonwood trunks selected as targets. Bark sprayed everywhere as the two horsemen fired their twenty shots without slowing their racing mounts.

Of the twenty bullets, twelve were dead hits. *That*, vowed Ben McCulloch, was shooting. The Colt revolvers passed from man to man. Ammunition played out before every Ranger had the opportunity to try the weapons. But, promised the captain, they could keep their shirts on a month or two. Some three hundred and fifty such pistols would reach Texas that winter. By spring the Ranger company should be able to wipe out any band of raiding Comanches.

Big Foot thought so. With his rifle, "Sweet Lips," and two such pistols, he said, he could handle a passel of redskins himself. Billy Anderson's eyes gleamed as he imagined being so well armed on future solitary stalks.

But Jack had counted his chickens too soon. The Republic of Texas received the shipment of Colt pistols in late December. But the weapons were turned over to the Texas Navy, not the Rangers.

Jack protested to President Lamar.

"It couldn't be helped, Captain," explained the Chief Executive. "First things come first." He added that the Texas Republic was forming an alliance with a revolutionary movement in the Mexican province of Yucatán. Texas would be paid eight thousand dollars per month for supplying naval assistance to the insurgents.

"Consequently," he continued, "our navy gets first chance at any armament we might purchase. Mr. Colt designed these revolvers for marines in the first place. But your company won't be forgotten, Captain Hays; I assure you of that. Certainly we'll be out of this financial crisis soon. The first available funds will be earmarked to order more weapons from Mr. Colt."

Jack rode dejectedly back to camp. He saw nothing to do but accept the disappointment.

5

Texas Routs the Invaders

Two frustrating years passed. Jack Hays, acknowledging presents for his twenty-fourth birthday, wrote his Mississippi kin that conditions were unchanged since his last letter. His Ranger troop still stormed into the hilly areas after raiding Comanche parties. Sometimes they overtook their quarries; more often they did not. Even less often they provoked a fight out of their savage adversaries. "Generally," he stated modestly, "we are able to best them. But just driving them off isn't a solution. I don't doubt that our harassed settlers feel that we have accomplished nothing in their behalf. But I have good reason to hope that things will take a turn for the better."

The good reason was his old idol, Houston. "The Raven" had never concealed his intention to seek a second term. Except for the constitutional limitation, he would never have allowed another man to hold the office. David G. Burnet opposed the ex-Tennessean. To the interested Jack, the bitter personality exchanges between the two men meant nothing at all. Houston, Hays was sure, would work more adroitly to get Texas under The Stars and Stripes.

Houston was elected by a heavy majority, and Jack attended the inauguration ceremony, on December 13,

1841, at Austin, the new capital. But "The Raven" refused to administer the government from there, and assembled his Cabinet at Washington-on-the-Brazos to be safe from "Comanches and buffalo stampedes."

There Jack rode in the early summer of 1842 to ask Presidential intervention in his company's behalf. The Republic's currency was worth only twenty-five cents on the dollar. His privates thus received the equivalent of ten dollars per month. How could men provide their own livelihood at such wages? Must he continue to solicit surveying assignments? His company would surely break up without supplementary earnings.

President Houston offered little encouragement. The Republic's debt now exceeded five million dollars. He had slashed every expense of government, including his own salary. This Texas debt was a major obstacle to annexation. The United States Whigs were making political hay of the indebtedness at every opportunity. The Texas government had to operate within its budget; military and naval costs would be cut to the bone.

Jack took the discouraging word back to camp. They would get neither wage increases nor their pay in gold. He'd hustle up surveying work, he promised, and they'd manage somehow. He hoped his company would hold together through the winter and early spring.

"Reckon we will," Sam said gruffly. "Things aren't any better anywhere else. We might as well stick it out."

Happily, it was a quiet winter. The Comanches apparently enjoyed good hunting in the upper Plains regions and staged few raids on the Texas settlements. But the first months of 1843 brought more and more signs of renewed Mexican hostility. Several San Antonio merchants of Mexican blood suddenly closed their businesses and left town.

Former mayor Juan Seguin departed from the Bexar scene in bitter dudgeon. *Banditos* redoubled their pillaging along the Frio and Nueces rivers.

San Antonio's committee of citizens appealed to President Houston to redouble the Ranger company. "The Raven" grimly refused. Texas was making headway in repairing its financial fences, he declared. Lone Star currency was worth fifty cents in United States money now. The President hoped Jack's company was sufficient to watch the Rio Grande. If invasion came, Texas would fight with volunteers, not regulars.

If invasion came! By summer the Rangers were as sure of it as the alarmed citizens of San Antonio. Jack assigned half of his company to patrol of the two *camino reals*. But his thin ranks could not spread out everywhere. August came—the worst of all months for Comanche forays. Red men struck at Castroville, Castell, Comfort, Fredericksburg. The Rangers almost wore out their horses trying to be everywhere at once.

Then, in the late afternoon of September 1, Walker, Woolfork, Wallace, and Davis saw a flash of activity along the Guerrero road.

Jack mounted a fresh horse and rode to scout the enemy himself, a half-dozen other grim men behind him. For almost six years, thought Jack, struggling against his fatigue, he had helped watch for such a Mexican movement northward. How many false rumors had sent the Rangers galloping out of San Antonio? On three occasions they had ridden all the way to Laredo. Other times they had found *bandito* forces kicking up a storm. These weren't *banditos*. These were fifteen hundred Mexican regulars. Jack learned that from a captured sentry. Wearing Mexican clothes, speaking Spanish, he and Sam slipped into the Mexican camp in the dark.

A French soldier of fortune commanded these invaders, General Adrian Woll.

Were reinforcements moving up from the Rio? Jack dispatched McCulloch and ten Rangers to find out while he galloped back to alert the San Antonio population. He roused the committee for a midnight session. By dawn he had Rangers fanning out in all directions and a courier speeding to inform President Houston of the approaching army. Then he rode back to Walker's patrol, which was heckling the Mexican advance as much as ten horsemen could hamper an army of such size.

Forty men against fifteen hundred! Any sort of stand was out of the question. But the Rangers could heckle Woll's advance, and did. They cut off and killed so many scouts that the French general stopped sending out patrols. No couriers escaped the thin circle of horsemen. Jack could assure the San Antonio committee that Woll was cut off from communications with the Rio Grande.

But this was small comfort to the distressed citizens. The enemy force moved into camp near San José Mission, five miles from the city limits. There was no reason not to expect an assault within forty-eight hours. Meanwhile a straggle of volunteers had reached Salado Creek. Matthew Caldwell seemed to be in their charge, but nobody was sure. No more than two hundred were ready to fight, and these had no sort of artillery. Jack felt it his place to pen a report to the Secretary of War. San Antonio, in his opinion, could not be defended. Until ordered otherwise, he meant to keep his company out of the town. His Rangers could not be wiped out as long as they kept to their saddles. Their horsemanship was at once their strongest weapon and their salvation.

He delivered a copy of his report to Caldwell, then rejoined his men on the San Antonio River. He rode up just in time to help Walker rout a Mexican wood-gathering detail. Then the Texans made their usual casual camp: they simply spread their blankets and slept like exhausted men. They would be up and riding before daylight anyhow.

Woll's army resumed its methodical advance next day. But just before ten o'clock a trio of officers rode out ahead of the main force bearing a white flag. Jack went alone to meet them. General Woll offered to spare the town if there was no resistance. Off galloped Jack to so inform the Bexar committee.

Back he rode in an hour to inform Woll that Texans would not defend the city. He led his company around San Antonio. From here on his troop was part and parcel of the Texan volunteer army, subject to the orders of General Caldwell.

The Texans had spread out along the Salado. He'd make a stand there, promised Caldwell. He was a heavy-set man, slow of speech and even slower of action, reminding Jack very much of Colonel Karnes. Obviously Caldwell meant to depend on his riflemen.

"Find a thicket, Captain," invited the general, "and hold it. That's what the rest of us mean to do. We're not backing up a step from here."

Jack hesitated, studying the terrain between the river and San Antonio. He was not critical of Caldwell's strategy; the best use of infantry was to station them behind cover and wait for an attack. But would General Woll send his dragoons across wide-open prairies to flush out the Texans? Some sort of deploying action was needed.

"If the general has no objections," Jack said carefully, "I'll keep my company mounted. I believe we can worry the enemy a little."

"Sure," Caldwell agreed quickly. "Bother the daylights out of him. Consider yourself on your own, Captain. You jaspers have your style of fighting—we have ours. Just remember, you're backed up with three hundred rifles."

Jack nodded. He'd remember. In fact, he rode off mulling over a plan to maneuver Woll into assaulting Caldwell's position.

The Frenchman marched into San Antonio to martial music—his own band.

"Never thought I'd see it," muttered Sam Walker. "The *hombre* must like music to bring a band all this distance."

Jack nodded. Europe-trained commanders considered a brass band essential to winning battles. He grinned as he looked along his own ranks. Big Foot Wallace could pluck a jew's-harp. Jack had heard Acklin scrape out a crude rendition of "Old Dan Tucker" on a borrowed fiddle.

"Want to play us a tune, Big Foot?" Jack asked.

The Virginian grunted and raised his rifle. " 'Sweet Lips' will put out all the music we need. Let them varmits just wait."

Watching from a safe distance, Jack admired the efficiency of Woll's troops. The Frenchman occupied San Antonio with as little fuss as possible. Artillery was set up on the walls of the Alamo. Patrols guarded every exit from the town. The Ranger captain grinned. Woll had learned all there was to know about regular military tactics. But what about enemy cavalry who patterned their horsemanship after Comanches? Jack sent Sam and a detail one way, led ten Rangers another. Simultaneously, both groups swooped down on outlying Mexican patrols. *Escopetas* blazed, but the Mexicans couldn't match a Texan's marksmanship. The big difference was in their guns. A Mexican carbine had too much recoil to allow a dead bead. As for Woll's canyon—could artillerymen aim shells at galloping, zig-zagging horsemen? Let the shells burst and scream.

The Rangers struck quickly, then dashed to safety as the outposts were reinforced, leaving a dozen dead. Sitting their saddles, the Texans waited for the opportunity to strike again.

Walker and McCulloch stole into San Antonio that night. Disguised as Mexican privates, they slipped into the very middle of Woll's camp, returning with the news that the Frenchman had offered a five-hundred-peso reward for the capture or death of Jack Hays.

"That's sure a heap of money," said Ben. "Makes you worth more in Mexico than you are in Texas. Here you can't even draw your pay."

"But it sure won't be easy to collect," said Big Foot. "Let's have another go at 'em at daylight, Jack."

Their captain nodded. He had already planned a dawn attack on all outposts. If General Woll wanted his head, let him send out enough lancers to get it.

This day the Mexicans revealed that they had received orders to pursue the will-of-the-wisps. Lancer companies rode back and forth waiting for Ranger attacks. Artillery from the Alamo boomed out the instant gunners sighted moving horsemen. Woll was getting impatient, all right. Jack rode back to Salado Creek. Caldwell had gained fifty new volunteers during the night. Just stay put, cautioned Jack. His company would draw Woll out of San Antonio —the Frenchman's cavalry anyhow. Sooner or later the general would tire of this ridiculous situation. Thirteen hundred regular troops beseiged by fifty nondescript horsemen!

Woll's professional pride demanded that he do something about such presumptuous assailants.

A day later and out they came—at least three hundred Mexican dragoons. They meant business too. Jack had carefully rehearsed Walker and McCulloch. Sam's detail clashed with the lancers first, then broke in apparent flight. Ben's handful of Rangers made a show of resistance, then crumpled too. Jack's group was already falling back. Mexican bugles signaled hard pursuit for the lancers. The Rangers scurried for the timber like foxes taking to cover.

Suddenly the woods belched fire at the charging dragoons, staggering them. Before the shocked Mexicans could rally, a second volley took grim toll of their ranks. Seeing the enemy's confusion, Jack ordered his troop to turn. They galloped down upon the disorganized dragoons, pistols blazing. The lancers forgot about ranks; many threw down their *escopetas*. They fled back to San Antonio in complete confusion. Artillery fire covered the last mile of their retreat. Jack balked at leading his company into cannon range.

The defeat apparently convinced Woll that he wasn't strong enough to reconquer Texas. The enemy abandoned San Antonio the next day, withdrawing warily. A full day was lost before Caldwell could organize his ranks for pursuit. The Texan volunteers had not counted on following the foe southward. Some of them didn't care for the idea.

This reluctance and indecision cost the Texans an opportunity to destroy the invaders. Reaching the Frio, Woll found the stream flooded by a recent rain. He set up artillery on the north bank to cover crossing of his troops.

Jack proposed that the Texans storm the temporary gun emplacements. "Let me have fifty volunteers," he proposed, "and we'll take the cannon. We'll have Woll's own guns on him."

Promised that many reinforcements, he led his Rangers against the artillery in a bold rush. Woll's gunners couldn't take sight on such swift-moving targets; their shells screamed over the Texans' heads, and the Rangers gained the dirt barricades with only one casualty. Kit Acklin quickly evened the score for his fallen comrade. He leaped from his galloping mustang and killed a gunner by shooting between a cannon's wheels. The Mexican infantry supposed to repulse such charges were ridden down or scattered.

Jack and his handful of men secured the cannon. The way was open for General Caldwell to attack. But no reinforcements came. For ten long minutes the Rangers held their position despite the rush of Mexican dragoons and infantry to recover the precious artillery. Then Jack ordered a retreat. His disgusted men followed him back.

"Owing to the boggy ground and tired horses," General Caldwell later stated officially, "I failed to support Captain Hays."

Jack kept his own counsel. He even walked away from his men so that he wouldn't be tempted to echo their grumbling. Woll was already safe across the Frio. The Texans could go through the motions of further pursuit, but why bother? Their only hope lay in swift-striking attack and Caldwell could never gear his volunteers for such a maneuver. When the general called a session of his captains, Jack quickly voted that they return to San Antonio and disband. The invader was driven out. They might as well settle for that.

6

Hays Stops at the Rio Grande

General Matthew Caldwell mustered out his troops in Alamo Plaza. Hundreds of spectators had gathered to watch; applause greeted each company's withdrawal from service. Hays and his Rangers took no part in the ceremony. Let the volunteers have this show to themselves as they shouldered their muskets and marched home to harvest late crops and clear more land.

Off they trudged. But the next day Jack realized that there were more men milling around San Antonio than had followed Woll to the Frio. Caldwell's volunteers had scattered, true; these were new arrivals—volunteers who had taken their time about responding to Woll's threat. Watching the clusters of idle men, Jack was reminded of the human confusion in the summer of 1836. How many men, like himself, had reached Texas too late for the fighting? There had been so many newcomers glutting the Army's ranks that Jack had needed political pull to become a private. He grinned ruefully as he recalled the unfriendly reception he had encountered in Nacogdoches.

Nearly 350 men had given Caldwell lip service. Less than a hundred had actually fired a shot, but there had been no real battle. The riot of Woll's company near the Salado had been the only mass action. Jack's company could have listed a hundred small skirmishes if their captain had wanted to keep records. He didn't. His report to the Secretary of War said only that his company had finished its service with Caldwell and was awaiting further orders. He expected no formal reply. The government might have its extravagances, but correspondence with Captain Hays was not one of them.

The human tide kept swelling. Two days later General Edward Burleson arrived with a company of thirty men from Bastrop. He mounted one of the Alamo's walls and soon had an enthusiastic audience. Cheers interrupted him again and again as he urged organization of an army to invade Mexico. It was not enough, he thundered, to drive the enemy back. Why not carry the war below the Rio Grande and fight it to a glorious end!

The milling men worried San Antonio's committee.

"There's a free fight breaking out every hour," stormed Samuel Maverick. "These men are broke too. Before long they'll start looting. Jack, you must do something."

Hays shook his head. He had no authority over these men, he pointed out. He commanded a Ranger company, a scout unit. Civil law was not part of their responsibility.

"Well, we'll petition the President to give you the necessary authority," Maverick declared. "There must be five hundred men here now. We're at their mercy if they should ever turn into a mob."

He and Mr. Riddle made a hurried trip to President Houston's temporary headquarters at Columbia and returned with Presidential orders putting Bexar County under martial law—with Major Hays in authority.

Major Hays! Jack blinked as he read the Presidential

decree. But there was no mistake. Maverick could verify the promotion.

"The President sent the order for your promotion while I was there," Maverick explained. "You'll get official notice before long. Meanwhile, Jack, you must get these men off the streets. They're ruining business for our merchants. Ladies won't push through that crowd to buy anything. And I'm afraid of what'll happen if there's any kind of an incident."

Jack sighed. This Presidential decree added police work to his company's responsibilities. "We'll try to keep order," he promised.

He discussed ways of restraining the idle men with Walker and McCulloch. Neither of them liked this new duty any better than their commander. But they helped Jack prepare placards in the plazas and saloons. The Rangers were now military policemen. Every man in Hays' company had authority to make arrests.

Major Hays rode San Antonio's winding streets on his chestnut horse. His men were scattered everywhere, most of them afoot. Keeping order in this crowded town was no part-time assignment. Resentments flamed up quickly. Texans weren't used to martial law. A few heads were cracked; two men were shot. But by the time Houston's call for volunteers reached San Antonio, the town was almost orderly. At least reluctant acceptance of the Rangers' authority had been established.

The President, yielding to public pressure, was calling for men to march on Mexico. He could not do otherwise, he said in an unofficial message to Jack. But he had considerable misgivings about such an expedition. The Republic of Texas had no business planning a large-scale conquest. The treasury had no funds to finance any invasion; but since hundreds of men seemed determined to try it, Houston would give them official recognition. He hoped, however, that Jack and cooler heads could keep the more exuberant spirits in line.

Jack took quick advantage of this unofficial message by ordering a roundup of all unemployed men in San Antonio. Those who wanted to enlist for the invasion were marched into camp on the Medina River. The others were curtly ordered to leave town.

Two weeks later, when General Alexander Somervell rode up to take official charge of the volunteers, he brought orders for Major Hays to command a scout battalion of 120 men, with his Rangers as a nucleus.

Two months later Jack Hays spread out his company to keep order again. The scene this time was along the banks of the Rio Grande near Guerrero. The occasion was Somervell's shocking order of December 19, 1842. The Texan commander announced his intention to march back to Gonzales and muster all of the volunteers out of service.

There had been grumbling before, even veiled threats and secret meetings, for nobody had liked the way Somervell had commanded this expedition. First, he had led the volunteers off the main road and through low-lying brush country made quagmires by heavy rains. They had found Laredo unoccupied by Mexican troops, but Somervell had decided not to cross the Rio Grande there. He had led his army eastward, following the winding river, until they had gone into camp at Guerrero.

Jack's company grumbled at his orders. Let Somervell protect his own hide. Sure, the rank and file of this Texan army was up in arms. Dick Fisher and Tom Green and

others were stirring up a hornets' nest. With good cause too.
What kind of blundering idiot was this man Somervell?

Jack spoke curtly: whatever their personal thoughts about
General Somervell, their duty was to keep order. They had
to hold down violence. If there was a march into Mexico
despite Somervell's order, he wouldn't try to stop any man
in his company. Shaking their heads, his men scattered
through the crowd. Jack watched them with a half-smile
playing about his lips. They'd obey him, all right. They'd
move quickly to help if Somervell's safety was threatened.

The general rode up on his bay horse. He spoke to the
angry men without dismounting. Somervell was cast from
the same mold as Karnes and Caldwell. As he faced his
dissenters calmly, it was clear that he wasn't easily ruffled.

"Hear me," he spoke out. "I have issued this order as
your commanding officer duly appointed by President Houston. It is my considered judgment that it would be folly for
us to attempt any invasion of Mexico at this time." Jeers
interrupted him; Somervell raised his hand. "Hear me out,"
he shouted, "then do as you please."

His raucous audience fell quiet again. "We have neither
the powder nor the supplies to sustain us in Mexico," Somervell continued. "Yesterday I dispatched Major Hays and his
Ranger company into Guerrero. I submitted a demand to
the *alcalde* for five thousand dollars or its equivalent in
livestock under threat of destroying the town. Major Hays
returned with the information that most of the citizens
have fled, taking their livestock with them. Even if we ran-
sacked every *jacal* in the town, we wouldn't get enough
meat to sustain us three days. You may look to Major Hays
for confirmation of that."

Jack nodded in support of the general's statements. The
Rangers had delivered Somervell's ultimatum. They knew

that it would be useless to occupy Guerrero—as pointless as their march into Laredo had been earlier in the month.

"We have very little powder," went on Somervell. "We could fight a battle, yes—but we couldn't wage another one until we had captured enemy supplies. I am as loyal a Texan as any of you, but I feel time and distance are against us."

Dick Fisher spoke up from the front ranks, "There's plenty who don't agree, General."

"You are entitled to your opinion, Captain Fisher," the man on the bay horse said crisply. Then to the assembled men again: "I realize that most of you enlisted with the understanding that we would fight in Mexico. I feel sure that President Houston would want me to release any company from service which doesn't want to return. I am doing so here and now. Those who wish to continue in the service of their country will march back with me to Gonzales and be discharged. Those who don't will be considered as being dismissed from the army here and now, and are free to go about any business they wish."

The general paused to let his listeners absorb the import of his words.

"But, General," protested Tom Green, "that'd make us out as sort of freebooters or filibusters—which we aren't. We joined up to take the Lone Star flag across the Rio Grande. That's what President Houston said we'd do."

A hundred or more grim men signified their approval of Green's words.

"That is true," answered Somervell. "But it is also true that Sam Houston has never led or sent a Texan army into certain disaster. Nor, as his appointed general, shall I."

There was another demonstration, one of angry disapproval. Fisher finally made himself heard above the uproar: "Let's get this straight, General: You're turning us loose. We can reorganize ourselves if we want."

"Yes," Somervell said. His eyes swept their faces. "I have nothing further to say," he announced. "Now you men can listen to Captain Fisher, Tom Green, or anybody you like. Or you can get ready to march back with me."

Through all of this, Jack had stood quietly a few paces from Somervell. Now attention was turned upon the major as the general rode off.

"How about it, Major Hays?" shouted a leather-lunged Texan. "Are you for Mexico or for going back?"

The question spread from lip to lip. Haranguing stopped while the five hundred volunteers waited for Jack to commit himself. He licked his lips. Somervell had taken this step without asking his advice. To Jack it seemed rather a foolish thing to do. The whole expedition seemed so, for that matter. But, standing hesitantly there, Jack thought he understood the reasons for Somervell's mismanagement of the invasion. Sam Houston had never wanted to attack Mexico in the first place. The President had not taken any sort of action until public opinion had forced his hand. Had Houston master-minded this whole affair? Had the President simply ordered them to organize and march out of San Antonio because he had not known any other way to dispose of them?

The crowd was stirring, impatient for Jack's answer. He gestured helplessly with his hands. How could he explain how he felt? His sympathies were with them. He would have liked nothing better than to lead his Ranger troop into Mexico, but he understood something about the complications of such an invision. It would have international implications. And, in political matters, he had no choice but to put his implicit trust in his fellow Tennessean. They had not come to Texas together, but they had come for the same reason.

"My circumstances are different from yours," he told the disgruntled volunteers. "I can't drop my responsibilities here on this river bank. I have to escort this army back to Gonzales regardless of how I feel about it." He took a deep breath. "You have heard the general," he added. "Those of you who wish can cross the river. That goes for my company. Every man must make his own choice."

A silence followed. Sam Walker finally spoke up: "What does all that palaver add up to, Jack?"

"You heard me," Jack said tonelessly. "I'm going back."

"And we can do as we please?"

"You can."

Sam hesitated, then turned to Dick Fisher. "No use of arguing with him," Sam said sadly. "When he says a thing, that's the way it is. But it's *bueno* with him for us to pick our own road." He hesitated, looking to Jack regretfully. "You'll have a Ranger company if you get enough volunteers," he added grimly.

"That's what I wanted to know," Fisher cried. "I'd hate to start into Mexico without Rangers."

Jack walked off. He meant it. Any Ranger who wished could follow Fisher into Mexico. Behind him he heard Sam call out: "You galoots who aim to get your feet wet hustle over here."

Thirty-one of the Rangers grouped around Walker. Over three hundred of the five hundred volunteers elected to cross the Rio with Fisher and Green.

Somervell was in a hurry to depart, and Jack took the lead immediately with the remaining handful of his men. Once he looked back to see what was happening. The Texans were grouped closely, as if electing a leader. Jack's lips tightened. Should he have tried to stop them? Could he have done anything if he had tried? He decided in the negative. There was no curbing such high-spirited men. They'd come this far to fight Mexicans and, by gum, they meant to do it. A suggestion of a smile formed about his lips. He could not censure them, but he could pity them a little, for he could not see them getting too far into Mexico.

They got as far as Mier, just downstream on the Mexican side. There they encountered superior odds and finally surrendered.

Alligator Davis brought the news to Jack a week later. Davis had been one of twenty men left behind to guard the Texan horses while the volunteers entered Mier afoot.

Most of his companions had escaped, he said. But at least a dozen Rangers were now Mexican prisoners, among them Walker, McCulloch, Acklin, Big Foot.

Several days later other escaped prisoners reached San Antonio, bringing word of the grim treatment at Salado. The Texans had been ordered to draw beans out of an earthen jar. The seventeen who had drawn black beans had been executed on the spot. The others had been marched into Mexico for imprisonment. Walker was alive, also Ben and Kit and Big Foot. But there was no telling when—or if—their commander would see them again.

7

Jack Frightens a Young Lady

It was a pleasant September afternoon in 1843. Jack Hays, riding alone for once, was in no hurry. He would reach Seguin shortly without driving his pony, and that was as far as he meant to travel that day.

His destination was Washington-on-the-Brazos, where President Houston had called Congress into special session. Jack's business was to make another appeal for funds. Without some relief he couldn't hold his troop together through the winter. Any piece of string was just so long, and—as Jack had informed the San Antonio citizens' committee the previous day—he had reached the end of his. He had a bundle of land certificates but no money. There was no question of slackening allegiance to Sam Houston or fading faith in Texas. He had just reached the end of his resources.

These last seven months of 1843 had exhausted his company physically as well as financially. The worst was over; the Comanches always fell back to their prairie hunting grounds with the coming of the late-summer rains. The Mexican border seemed quiet too, especially after the Ranger victory over *bandito* Antonio Perez. Jack and fifteen companions had wiped out Perez's gang in a two-day running battle on the Medina River. All indications pointed to a calm winter, especially with rumors flying of an official armistice between Texas and Mexico. Now, Jack had decided, it was high time to get down to his own business.

He rode into Seguin before sundown. Mrs. Riddle had asked him to do an errand and Jack decided to get this out of the way before hunting accommodations for the night. A Judge Jeremiah Calvert and his family had recently moved from Alabama to the pleasant town on the Guadalupe, and Mrs. Riddle wanted the Calverts to visit her during the Christmas season.

"They'd find it easy to decline a written invitation," the San Antonio matron had explained. "So you act as my spokesman, Jack—and don't take 'no' for an answer. You can persuade them."

Terror he was to the Comanche Indians and "Devil Jack" to the Mexicans, but to San Antonio's ladies he was a "nice young man" to fuss over and order about.

He located the Calvert house without difficulty. It was newly finished that summer, gleaming white with a design that reminded him of "The Hermitage." He dismounted, tethered his horse, and studied the house front. Looking at the tall, white pillars and high slanted roof, Jack found it easy to believe that Judge Calvert had lived recently in the South.

The major had ridden into Seguin without changing his clothes or taking his pistols out of his belt. Sun-browned, slight in stature, head shaded by a straw sombrero—why shouldn't the young lady stepping suddenly around a corner of the house decide that she faced a Mexican trespasser!

She stood rooted in her tracks a moment, her eyes wide with fright.

"You—go—away!"

Each word represented a herculean struggle for Susan

Calvert. Having pronounced them, she turned and fled.

Jack stared after her. As he paused there uncertainly, the front door opened and there stood a dignified, middle-aged man in broadcloth suit and white linen.

"What is it?" he snapped. "State your business and be gone."

Jack's smile formed slowly. "Are you Judge Calvert, sir?"

"I am."

"My name is Hays, sir, Jack Hays. Mrs. Riddle of San Antonio asked me to deliver a message."

The dignified man frowned. "Jack Hays?" he asked slowly. "Not *the* Major Jack Hays!"

"Yes, sir." Jack shifted his weight from one foot to the other. "I'm on my way to the capital, sir, and Mrs. Riddle asked me to stop by."

Judge Calvert was convinced now. A chuckle came from behind his white beard.

"For which," he said heartily, holding out his hand, "we will be forever grateful to Mrs. Riddle. Jack Hays! Why, sir——"

He shook his head and his chuckle swelled into a laugh. "I should apologize, and I will. So shall my daughter, Susan, if she ever gets her wits back. But there is some justification for her attitude, sir. Indeed there is. A stranger dismounts at our door, a young stranger. And we don't know him for Jack Hays at all. Of course she didn't. Why should I? Jack Hays should stand ten feet tall."

Then the jocularity left his voice. "Welcome to my home, Major. Very proudly I bid you welcome. Now if you can forgive our rude reception and be our guest . . ."

Jack hesitated.

"I'm only riding through town, sir. Mrs. Riddle's message——"

"Can wait," insisted Judge Calvert, "or at least can be delivered over a mint julep. It isn't every day, sir, that we can receive a military hero."

"I'm afraid you flatter me, Judge."

"Do I?" asked Calvert with another chuckle. "Then you have flattery coming to you from every corner of Texas, young man."

He ushered Jack into the comfortable reception room and ordered a servant to bring refreshments.

"And tell Miss Susan it's safe to come downstairs," the judge added, eyes twinkling. "Tell her our guest is Major Jack Hays of the Texas Rangers."

Susan Calvert graciously offered her apologies. Then she quickly put the stammering, embarrassed visitor at ease. She joined her father in inviting him to remain for the night, but Jack insisted he must ride on. He suddenly realized he had no other clothes, and he could hardly visit in such a household in his present regalia.

He took his leave with genuine regret, but it was easy for him to promise that he would return. Susan Calvert . . . how long since he had met such an attractive young lady? Such poise and charm! With a sigh Jack prodded his pony toward Seguin's only inn. He might as well forget such thoughts for the time being. In spite of any fuss over his military accomplishments, he was still an impoverished man.

He entered the inn and was asking about accommodations when a voice suddenly came from across the lobby:

"Major Jack Hays?"

He turned to face a stocky, friendly man in linen duster and gray suit. "Yes, sir?"

"By heaven, this is fortunate!" exclaimed the other, holding out his hand. "You probably don't know me: I am

Congressman W. G. Cooke. Believe it or not, Major, I was on my way to San Antonio to see you."

Jack returned the handshake. He knew of Congressman Cooke by reputation. "To see me, sir?"

"I certainly was," the congressman said heartily. He took out a thick wallet. "I have a package for you. Congress has just adjourned. And one of our last actions was to vote you a special appropriation to reimburse you, at least partially, for your personal expenditures in defense of Texas. Here, sir, is a government draft for one thousand dollars, and another to cover back wages for your great Rangers." Cooke hesitated, then added with a rueful smile: "And for once, Major, a draft on the Republic of Texas is worth face value. Sam Houston has kept his word to the people of Texas—we are almost a solvent nation again."

For a moment Jack could not believe it. But he held the proof in his hand. A draft on the Republic of Texas for one thousand dollars! Another draft to cover all the wages due his company!

He insisted on shaking hands with Congressman Cooke again.

"You don't realize, sir," he said a little huskily, "how much this means to me."

"I think I do, Major," Cooke said quietly. "I believe President Houston does, and Congress as well. I'm a member of our Military Appropriations Committee; the chairman instructed me to deliver these funds to you at once." He clapped Jack on the shoulder. "My instructions didn't specify that I invite you to dinner also," he added, "but I insist on it. I have another bit of welcome news."

"This is almost too much," Jack said, patting the wallet. "Don't overwhelm me."

"I'm afraid I must," Cooke said, leading him into the

dining room. "And I've never performed a happier duty for the Republic of Texas. I understand, Major, that you had a great deal to do with Texas' purchasing some repeating revolvers from Samuel Colt?"

"I had something to do with it," Jack said truthfully. "But actually it was Sam Walker who proposed the changes and——"

"I know," interrupted the congressman. "But the weapons were turned over to the navy by the previous administration. Our navy is now in dry-dock at Galveston, Major. President Houston has finally succeeded in getting our ships home."

Cooke's eyes twinkled at Jack across the gleaming white tablecloth. "And I'm happy to inform you," he continued, "that the Colt five-shooters are now on their way to your camp at San Antonio. You should have them by next week at the latest. And there's enough ammunition for your company to put on quite a campaign the next time you go after the Mexicans or the Comanches."

Jack's eyes gleamed. That was even better news than the personal appropriation of money.

He shook his shaggy head. "That will make a great difference," he said softly. "I was afraid my troop would quit on me this winter, Mr. Cooke. But with their back pay and the new guns . . ." he grinned. "I don't reckon we'll ever stop now."

"Texas couldn't do without your company, Major," declared the congressman. "We know it at the capital, from President Houston down to the youngest pageboy." He leaned back at his chair and smiled at his guest. "Now how about a day or so of relaxation, Major? Have you met any of our fine Seguin citizens?"

"One family, the Calverts. I stopped by their house to deliver a message."

"Excellent!" approved Cooke. "A fine Southern gentleman. I am going to a small reception there tonight."

"I know," nodded Jack. "Judge Calvert was kind enough to invite me."

"And you aren't going?"

"No, sir."

"Why not, Major? Don't you ever relax in convivial company."

"Yes, sir, when the chance comes." Jack shrugged his shoulders. "But I've no other clothes and——"

"Nonsense," Cooke said impatiently. "You can wear a suit of mine. Or, better still, I'll take you right down to Griffin's Store. He's a fine merchant and his stock compares with anything in Houston."

Jack nodded, thinking of his sudden wealth. "I'd like that," he decided. "I need a presentable suit." He grinned a little sheepishly. "You know, Mr. Cooke, I haven't owned a dress suit in six years."

The congressman studied him suspiciously. "You can't be serious, Major?"

"But I am," Jack said quietly. "I haven't had the money to buy new clothes. Not for dress occasions."

"Texas has neglected you too long," declared Congressman Cooke. "Tonight we shall make partial amends. Put yourself in my hands, Major. I promise you a most pleasant evening."

And it was. Judge Calvert had planned only a small informal reception. But by eight o'clock his guest list had increased to forty, with every reason to expect more.

"We are suddenly the most popular family in town," he

said ruefully but also with pride. "The word has spread everywhere that Jack Hays will be here. I gather that the whole area wants to meet him face to face and shake his hand."

Susan, the judge noticed, had not failed to don her most becoming gown and to take particular pains with her brown wavy hair. Her father, however, did not believe she would form any romantic attachment for the noted warrior. Susan's taste ran to gentle, refined men, not doughty soldiers. The very ruggedness of Hays' career would discourage her.

Then Congressman Cooke brought his guest and Judge Calvert was completely surprised at the transformation. Jack had selected a broadcloth suit of conservative cut, a white shirt, and plain black tie. A barber had managed to subdue his shock of brown hair. Standing in the middle of an admiring circle, blushing at the extravagant compliments of Mr. Calvert's other guests, he looked more like a young lawyer or doctor than a frontier hero.

Susan reacted the same way—her father saw that clearly. A puzzled expression showed in her eyes when her glance met that of their celebrated guest. She is wondering about him, mused the Judge, trying to assemble her varied impressions into a positive feeling.

Not until almost ten o'clock did Susan and Jack talk with any privacy. When a group that had driven twenty miles to meet the Ranger leader departed, Susan saw them to the door and Jack shook hands with every member of the group. Judge Calvert escorted the departing guests to their carriages. Susan, turning away from the door, found herself standing next to Jack.

"You are very gracious to our guests, Major Hays," she said softly. "My father and I appreciate it."

"I'm enjoying it," Jack said quickly. "I don't get to mingle with such nice people very often. Gatherings like this make me a little homesick."

"Where is your home?"

"I haven't any—now. I was thinking about Tennessee when I said that. My father's home, and my uncle's. Almost every Sunday we used to go over to my uncle's. The whole family. And there'd be dozens of other people there—some of them relatives, others friends. I was only a boy then, but I can still remember those get-togethers."

"Who was your uncle?"

"Andrew Jackson."

"Andrew Jackson!" Susan's face showed her surprise. "I didn't know that. I'm sure Father didn't either."

Jack looked away, embarrassed. "I haven't traded on his reputation much," he murmured.

"No," Susan said after a moment. "You haven't found it necessary." Her eyes danced. "But you didn't tell me as a secret, sir, and I won't keep it a secret."

"There's no reason to," he smiled. "I'm certainly not ashamed of it."

"I should think not." Susan hesitated, then said, "If you have enjoyed yourself, sir, you must come again. Any time."

His hazel eyes studied her face. It was Susan's first experience with his level, intent look. Flecks of crimson showed in his cheeks.

"I mean it, Major Hays," she said lightly.

Jack nodded after another moment of the same grave study. "I hope you do," he said. "For I certainly intend to come again."

8

Lightning Hits the Comanches

Jack hesitated between two choices the next morning. Should he ride back immediately with his company's payroll or follow up the previous evening with a personal call upon Miss Calvert? The former won out. He couldn't put pleasure ahead of duty—especially not such overdue duty. But, he promised himself, this would not be his last trip to Seguin.

He reached the camp before noon. Alsey Miller was the first to learn it was payday.

"Glory be the highest!" exclaimed Alsey. "What'll we do with money—real money?"

The other Rangers were equally jubilant, especially when San Antonio merchants accepted the warrants at face value. By nightfall half of the company boasted new garments. Acklin and Billy Anderson were taunted because of their greasy buckskin regalia. Kit had an excuse: he could find neither shirt nor trousers to fit him. "Trouble is," he said, "they don't make man-sized breeches in this country." Bearded Billy shrugged off the twitting. Having worn buckskin before these young squirts were born, he was not about to change his ways.

Jack made no mention of the five-shooters. Once before,

he had advertised their acquisition and had been sorely disappointed. This time he would count only the birds in hand. But he stayed close to camp, waiting, and three days later a loaded Conestoga creaked toward the willows. His heart beating like a trip-hammer, Jack signed a receipt for 227 Colt revolvers and ammunition. The Texas Navy hadn't wasted many bullets, at least.

One by one, their weathered faces glowing, the Rangers were issued pistols: two to each man and more ammunition than could be carried in a wallet or shallow pockets. There was a rush on the venerable Mexican saddle-maker. He worker from early to late on heavy belts and leather pouches. The rattle of gunfire sounded from dawn to dark along the Medina. By early spring, vowed Jack, he'd have a company of crack pistol shots ready to take the field.

Together he and Sam Walker had learned a few tricks about the heavy weapons. One was to raise the gun to aim, not lower it. Another was to use the hammer for firing, not the trigger. The latter action was too slow. Speed of firing was important, along with accuracy. Sam had coined a phrase for it: "Don't just shoot 'em, sallivate 'em."

In mid-December Jack attended a meeting of the Bexar citizens' committee. The group was degenerating into a social club, complained Samuel Maverick. True enough, there seemed fewer Comanches than in any recent winter, and only the usual false alarms reached San Antonio about Mexican activity along the border.

"But we mustn't forget," Maverick stressed, "that we had a six-year respite from invasion and then, presto, there came Woll's army."

Major Hays concurred. They must not depend on rumors of an official armistice between Texas and Mexico. He was testing volunteers, he told the committee, and hoped to double the size of his company. He purposely omitted any mention of their new weapons or their new style of warfare. Let no such news reach either Mexicans or Comanches.

He returned to camp rather late. Mrs. Maverick had insisted he visit briefly after the meeting. With suitable clothes and cash to spend, Jack was mingling with people more. He had even called upon an eligible young lady, but had not been interested. He kept thinking of Susan Calvert the entire evening.

Acklin called out to him as he turned his horse loose to graze. "Feller here wants to see you, Jack."

Jack saw that Kit had company beside his small fire. In fact, several men squatted there on their haunches.

"What's up?" asked Jack, walking toward Kit's lean-to.

Acklin rose up. "Feller here says you don't know beans about handling a five-shooter, Jack. Says all you know is what he taught you—and he's not so hot a teacher."

Another man stood up too. Jack stopped short. Could he believe his own eyes? He let out a whoop and leaped to grab Sam Walker by the neck. Taking Walker by surprise, he flipped Sam backward and sat on him.

"We'll keep this varmint hog-tied," he declared. "We'll teach him not to go gallivanting off into Mexico."

Sam Walker, true enough! How had he escaped?

Yes, he'd been marched to Perote with the rest of the Mier captives. His guns had been taken away from him. A grin split his leathery face as he accepted new ones.

McCulloch—Big Foot Wallace—Buck Bailey—Mike Chevaille . . . Sam shook his head. As far as he knew, they were still in Perote Prison. But in Mexico the prisoners had heard talk of their early release. Jack nodded. He had heard such rumors too. Supposedly the French and British governments were pressuring Santa Anna to turn loose the

Texans. But that, as far as Jack was concerned, was like the talk of an official armistice between Texas and Mexico. He didn't know and he wasn't supposed to know.

"Hang it all, Sam, how did you slip away from them? How in tarnation did you manage it back to Texas?"

They pulled it out of him finally—but only in snatches.

"There was this *hombre* named Bill Thompson," Sam reluctantly explained. "He was hit in the leg during the fighting. He sat down and said, heck, no, he wasn't going to march. Just balked. They could shoot him if they wanted to, but he wouldn't stir a step."

He took a deep breath—how Walker hated to go into details. "Well, sir, the Mexicans didn't shoot him. They even took to treating him human. They let him ride a donkey all the way to Perote. His leg wasn't that bad either. He kept it all wrapped it up just to fool 'em. Down there they put us to work on a public road. Made us haul carts of dirts like jackasses—all but Thompson. 'Limping Bill,' we took to calling him. He'd sit and watch us work and never let on he was as able as any of us. We never squealed."

Another sigh. "He took his own sweet time limping back into the prison at night. The guards got to where they paid him little or no attention. They didn't squawk when Howard and I started helping him up the hill every night. They let us hang behind the rest because they figgered we were helping the hurt man." A grin split his lean face. "That's where they were wrong. We were watching 'em like hawks. Every day Limping Bill was harder to get up the hill. Finally we took off. Dived into the brush like sage hens."

He refilled his coffee cup, then went on: "We split up. Figgered we had a better chance that way. I ducked from *pueblo* to *pueblo*. Held up *jacals* for grub and a mule.

Pulled a serape low over my head and rubbed ashes in my face and hair. Nobody jumped me till I got plumb to Guerrero. It was too late then. I jumped off that old mule and gave 'em a run for the river. I hit the water lickety-splash and that's all she wrote."

And never again would he discuss his escape from Perote Prison.

"I'm sure glad you're back," Hays told Sam awkwardly. "I've needed some help with these jaspers. They can shoot a little, but they're not ready for the Comanches."

But by spring they were. By the spring of 1844 the Rangers rode the Pedernales Hills looking for Indians to fight. This, Jack had vowed, would be a summer the Comanches would long remember. Now the Texans would not wait for savages to strike before going into action. They would meet the red men in their own element—the open country.

Raiding parties came, all right. Dry summer brought them galloping south of the Cap Rock.

The war party was well over a hundred strong. Whooping wildly, they tore down from the ridges on the closed circle of white men. Jack ordered his Rangers to meet this first assault as usual, with their rifles. There was still an advantage of long guns—longer range and better markmanship. The Texans staggered the Comanche surge with their cool, withering fire. Undismayed, the savages re-formed and charged in for hand-to-hand combat.

Once the ordeal of rifle fire was over, the Indians expected to have things their own way. On whirling ponies they could throw lances and wield tomahawks more effectively than dismounted men could swing rifle butts or slash with bowie knives.

But these Texans, of a sudden, were mounted themselves! These startling warriors dropped rifles and took to their mustangs and met the Comanche surge head-on! From fifteen to twenty paces away came their blistering pistol fire. No one shot per man either. The Indians found themselves charging into a hail of bullets.

Comanches dropped like acorns. The dazed Indians jerked their ponies around and tried to flee. But there was no getting away from these white men. The Rangers could reload their revolvers as they rode. Each yelling white demon could shoot ten times while a desperate Indian threw one spear—his last. That lance hurled, the Comanche had only his tomahawk—a poor weapon from horseback. After several bounds of his mustang, the Ranger had ten more bullets.

Nor could the Indians elude the white man's pursuit. The Rangers rode mustangs too, and fresher ponies at that. There was no escaping them in the arroyos or ridges.

The Comanche ranks fell apart as small parties galloped wildly in all directions. Another Indian war force found itself caught up in the wild battle. It was raging all around them before the new arrivals knew where or why. They were never able to make a stand either. Jack, carefully preparing his report to the Secretary of War, estimated that his company killed a hundred warriors that June day.

And that was only the first victory of that summer. Two other Comanche parties were routed before reaching the hill country. Their day of raiding defenseless settlements along the Pedernales was over. From here on, they wouldn't even get within striking distance.

Jack kept his troop out until early September, then returned to San Antonio for more ammunition and supplies.

He had hardly dismounted before two burly men charged out to greet him. Big Foot Wallace and McCulloch were ready for duty again! The following week saw Mike Chevaille riding into camp on a borrowed horse. McCulloch claimed that he was "soft" and wangled patrol duty along the river. Walker led a detail to explore along the *camino reals.*

Jack saw them off with a sigh and rode into town. With nearly eighty men and two such lieutenants, he could afford leisure.

Mrs. Elizabeth Riddle called to him as he was crossing Alamo Plaza. He went sheepishly to her buggy, anticipating her scolding for avoiding all social activities since spring. Did he think he could keep his friends when he was always too busy to accept their invitations? He pleaded guilty at once.

"I'll do better," he promised. "By Christmas you'll be tired of having me around."

A smile played across her face. "You'd better change your tune," she threatened. "I'm expecting company from out of town next week. It wouldn't do for me to ignore you as completely as you have us."

"Not the Calverts!"

Mrs. Riddle tossed her dark head. "I'm not saying," she teased. "I'm not saying another word, not until tomorrow night. If you're our dinner guest then, I may tell you what I know about it. And again I might not. You're not the only eligible bachelor in Texas, Major Hays."

"No," he admitted, "but I'm the most helpless one."

"And you'll stay that way," she said a little sharply, "until you realize one thing: You can't do all the riding and fighting for this country. Not if you want to have a wife and family."

She drove away, leaving Jack to look after her thoughtfully. There was no denying that she had spoken the truth. In nearly eight years he had accumulated some land certificates, and that was all. That wasn't the tradition of his family. That wasn't the spirit in which his grandfather had moved into western Tennessee. And his Uncle Andrew—between wars "Old Hickory" had managed to accumulate a plantation and personal wealth as well as launch an epic political career. Jack rode slowly back to camp. It wasn't enough to be a hero of frontier wars; he must start concerning himself with his own future.

Mrs. Riddle's visitors were the Calverts, of course—the judge for only a day and night, his daughter for an indefinite stay. The social amenities in their honor began with an informal reception. Next came a ball, and Susan Calvert accepted Major Hays as her escort.

"I'm so glad," approved Susan's hostess. "I was afraid you wouldn't. I was afraid you hadn't seen enough of Jack Hays to appreciate him."

"Why," stammered the young woman, "I like him very much."

"You'll like him better," nodded Mrs. Riddle. She laughed softly. "In some ways he is such a boy. He will blush at the slightest excuse and it's easy to get him confused. But think over his life and you'll understand why. He's practically lived in the saddle for eight years; yet he is still a quiet gentleman. We like to think in San Antonio that no other man could have kept us from being murdered in our beds."

Susan nodded, a little flustered by her hostess' fervor.

It was a gay week for the visitor from Seguin. Next Mrs. Maverick held an entertainment in her honor. Her fete was in the form of a picnic under the trees along the San

Antonio River. Her proposal for entertainment was contests of horsemanship between Rangers and native *charros*.

Was she thinking to present the slim major in his best light? If so, she succeeded. Susan Calvert gasped again and again as her escort outdid the *charros* in daredevil stunts. She had never before seen horsemen scoop objects off the ground at a dead run, vault in and out of the saddle, slide under their mount's bellies while the animals kept galloping.

Then twilight brought an abrupt change of tempo. The *charros* became *caballeros*, strumming on their soft guitars, mixing romantic songs with lively airs. Susan was pulled to her feet and initiated into the fandango. She applauded the company's rendition of the Mexican Hat Dance. She learned fragments of *"Cieleto Liento."* Every Ranger, it seemed, danced well. Even Big Foot Wallace and Alligator Davis performed buck-and-wings.

It was midnight when the caravan returned to San Antonio's King William Street. Susan was exhausted, as a girl who had danced and applauded so much should be. But her happiness more than made up for her fatigue.

"I don't know when I've had such a thrilling evening," she gratefully told her escort.

Jack nodded. There had never been a picnic to compare with this one.

"I must tell my friends in Seguin, but they won't believe me."

"Why not?"

She waved her hands. "Your Rangers are famous, sir— but not for dancing quadrilles and fandangos. Who'll believe I danced with such soldiers as Sam Walker and Ben McCulloch, much less Jack Hays?"

"If anyone doubts it," he said with a grin, "I'll bring my company over to Seguin and prove it."

"Bring your men," she challenged. "You'll have a gala time."

"Yes," he said quietly. "Your being there will ensure that."

Susan bit her lip. "I'd better go inside," she said shyly. Jack Hays nodded. Yes, she had better go inside. For words were forming on his lips that he must not utter. He could not ask this beautiful, charming girl to share his life until he had something to offer—something other than a brush lean-to on the Medina River, a fast mustang, and a pair of deadly five-shooters.

"You said once I could come and visit you," he said. "Would I still be welcome?"

Her eyelids fluttered. "You will be welcome any time, Major Hays," she said softly.

The next week found him in Washington-on-the-Brazos. Taking stock of his land certificates, he found that he could claim some twelve thousand acres. Such land must be in the public domain and necessarily would be located some distance from a town. But Jack had no doubts about Susan's willingness to share a humble beginning. She would help any man she married make a start in life. Nor would she deplore the years Jack had postponed that beginning. He had taken on a responsibility; she was proud of the way he had met it. Her every word and gesture assured him of that.

Now it was time to relinquish that responsibility to another man. So Jack quietly explained to President Houston.

"The Raven" listened gravely, nodding several times.

His eyes twinkled when Jack explained that he wanted to put himself in a position to propose marriage.

"Have you picked her out yet?" the President asked.

"Yes, sir." Jack hesitated. "Miss Susan Calvert of Seguin, General," he added carefully. "But I haven't asked her. I may be talking out of turn."

"You don't want to ask her until you get your affairs in better order?"

"That's right, sir." Jack looked down at his dusty boots and homespun clothes. "I can't ask her to share this, General."

"No, of course not," conceded Houston. He took out his jackknife and a piece of pine wood. "Lad, I hate to discourage you," he said slowly, "but now is not the time to resign. Do you know what's happening in the United States?"

"What do you mean, sir?"

"Politics were never your forte," the President said somewhat drily. "You're so busy riding and fighting that you can't keep up with political tides. Maybe that's just as well. Fighting men such as you enable men like me to weave our political schemes. The United States will elect a president this year, lad. The Democrats have nominated James K. Polk of our former state, Tennessee. The annexation of Texas is the main plank in their platform. If Polk is elected—and the Democrats get Congress—we will go into the Union next year."

"Indeed, sir!"

"Indeed, sir," Houston said vigorously. "And as a bride arrayed for the altar, not a humble suppliant. Texas will go into the Union freely and proudly. That's what we've wanted, isn't it?"

"Yes, sir," Jack said heartily.

Houston went back to his whittling. "It is most important that we play our hand carefully in these next few months. We boast today that we are a nation that can defend itself. Your victories over the Comanches this summer are cited by the Democrats at every rally. Look at what Hays has done, they say, for proof that the Texans are winning their own frontier. Newspapers and other periodicals have printed glowing descriptions of what your company can accomplish with the five-shooters. Texas is at peace, say the Democrats. London and Paris and Washington are just as impressed. They are offering military alliances if we do not join the Union. And what does this vaunted peace of ours depend on for maintenance? One battalion of frontier fighters. One troop of Rangers. And, I'm very much afraid, on the magic of one man's name. If Jack Hays should ride off, what would happen to that company?"

"Why, nothing," Jack said quietly. "Both Walker and McCulloch are competent leaders. They are——"

"Yes," said Houston with a shrug, "but Jack Hays has become more than that. You underestimate the impact of personal fame, my boy. To the world, Jack Hays and the Rangers are one and the same. No doubt the Comanches would verify my claim. The red men are awed by 'Devil Jack.' They don't hold Walker and McCulloch in the same fear. They might come storming out of the prairies by the thousands and everything would fall around us like a house of cards."

The President handed Jack his carving—a miniature figure on horseback. "Wait until after the election," he urged. "If there isn't a Democratic victory, then go ahead. Turn over your command to whom you please and go about your business. But if Polk wins, stay in until the finish—

until the Lone Star flag comes down. You can manage that, can't you, lad?"

"I suppose I can," Jack said unhappily.

"Tell the young lady what you're up against," suggested Houston. "Let her share your role in destiny."

9

The End of a Nation

Never, Jack was sure, had time passed so slowly, nor human events moved so deliberately. It was October, 1844, when he promised Sam Houston to keep his command until annexation was decided. It had been an easy promise to give. So logical too. But fulfillment was anything but easy.

The election in the United States provided short suspense. It was held in November, but the results were not known at once—not in Texas at any rate. It was mid-December before Hays was certain that James K. Polk had been elected. The United States had given a convincing majority to both the candidate and his platform. The Democrats would have a firm grip on the next Congress. There was little chance that a bill offering annexation of the Lone Star nation would be voted down.

Jack lost little time in riding to Seguin. As yet he had not learned Judge Calvert's attitude toward him as a prospective son-in-law. Tradition required that he ask parental approval before making formal suit, and Hays had no intention of flouting this custom. It never occurred to him as he waited nervously in the judge's reception room that he had cast aside most other conventions of his boyhood. A new type of horse, new weapons, and a new mode of warfare, new garments, and a new dialect, embracing many Spanish words—he was anything but the average young Southerner of twenty-seven. Even his ideas as to the use of his twelve thousand acres were different. He owned no slaves and wanted none. He had no intention of becoming a typical planter. Never would he depend upon production of cotton for a livelihood.

Judge Calvert realized those differences. The dignified, bearded gentleman from Alabama knew that his daughter would have to make many adjustments in order to live happily as Mrs. Jack Hays.

"But that's her decision to make," her father said carefully. "I think it would be wise, sir, if you discussed your prospects with her. You cut an unusual figure, Major. Your utter simplicity is confusing. I hope Susan has neither underestimated you nor has been dazzled by your accomplishments."

Jack sighed. So did the judge.

"But if it is my permission you need," he continued, "you have it." He smiled. "I will defer any blessing until Susan's feelings are made known. She is the one who must live with you, not I."

Jack had parental permission to approach the lively Susan —but opportunity was something else. His visits to Seguin had to be brief and seldom. He still had responsibilities of command. The Comanches hadn't stopped raiding because of Polk's election. In fact, rumors of savage war parties reached San Antonio every few days. The red men were not striking the settlements; that winter they seemed to be venting their fury on Mexican villages along the Rio —Guerrero, Roma, San Aguinaldo. They had to be watched, nevertheless. And the congregation of strong Mexican garrisons required close attention. Purportedly these border reinforcements were to curtail the troublesome Indians. But neither Hays nor anyone else could be sure. Woll's invasion had come as a bolt out of the blue too.

Then there were his land negotiations. He converted his certificates into actual locations, then looked around for trades. He had clear-cut ideas as to what he wanted. The property must be near enough to San Antonio for him to live there; he could not ask Susan Calvert to share a frontier cabin.

It was Christmas before he realized it. A hurried visit to the Calverts left him only more dejected. Theirs was a typical family Yuletide, except for one innovation. The German immigrants had introduced the Christmas tree to Texas and, as a sort of special guest, he was permitted to help trim the tree.

Mrs. Riddle gave him small sympathy.

"You haven't asked her yet," that lady pointed out. "It's high time you got into action, young man. That girl is a prize. She won't twiddle her thumbs forever while you're trying to get up your nerve." Her tone softened. "Jack, I'm ashamed of you. You're scared to ask her—scared to death. Is it any harder than charging into Comanches?"

"A lot harder," Jack claimed.

Mrs. Riddle sighed. "I can't do it for you," she declared.

Mrs. Riddle was right, Jack decided. He must meet this crisis himself. Back he rode to Seguin on New Year's Eve. Susan was not expecting him, and had accepted an invitation to a ball at a nearby plantation.

"I'm very sorry," she said. "I wish I had known you were coming."

Jack nodded glumly. He should have let her know, of course. He shouldn't have barged into her home on New Year's Eve.

They sat in the spacious Calvert parlor. Susan laid a gentle hand on his arm. "I must go up and get dressed now, Major," she said apologetically.

He rose. "I know you must," he told her regretfully. "I apologize for coming over here this way. But it's New Year's Eve and tomorrow starts another year." He shifted his weight and toyed with the brim of his hat. "It looks like," he added, "Texas will be voted into the Union next year."

Susan nodded. "Yes, And I'll be so glad. I don't suppose I'll even realize the difference, but I'll be happier."

Jack took a deep breath. "It'll make a difference to me," he said. "A big difference. It'll mean I can resign. It'll mean there won't be any Rangers. I'll be free to think about——"

"Yes?" Susan prompted as his voice dropped.

"—about developing my land," Jack went on desperately. "And getting married."

There, he'd brought up the subject! He'd sounded the bugle call to action.

Susan looked away. "It's time," she said faintly, "you were thinking about that."

"It sure is," Jack agreed. "And thinking about that— when I do—which is every chance I get—I never think about anybody but you, Susan."

Her lips formed into a smile. Her eyes turned to meet his. "Are you proposing, Major Hays, by any chance?"

"No, ma'am," he said quickly. "Not by any chance. I'm doing it on purpose—or trying to." He shook his head. "I'm just not very good at this sort of palaver."

Susan Calvert slowly shook her head. "You aren't," she said with a choke in her voice. "It's a good thing too."

"Why is that?"

"Because," she replied, shaking her tears away, "I'm no hand for palaver either, Major Hays. I'm accepting, and I'm not sure how to do it."

Now he could endure the drag of time. Let the cumbersome motion of government delay their wedding if it must. At least he did not brood any longer over his doubtful prospects. Susan Calvert had spoken, and she verified that promise every time he saw her. These delaying processes— he could live with them. Such as the Texas plebiscite on annexation into the Union. The voters of Texas had three alternatives: First, they could vote out any sort of alliance. Or they could choose between joining the United States or continuing as a free country with the military support of England and France. Sam Houston's successor, Dr. Anson Jones, presented these options to his people. But few Texans gave the European alliance another thought. The Congress of the United States voted early in 1845 to offer annexation. By spring Texans had accepted in overwhelming numbers. By summer Texas had chosen delegates to frame a state constitution. The Ranger company guarded this convention at Austin. Nobody thought it likely that Comanches would disturb these statesmen, but the Rangers kept watch anyhow.

Off went the drafted constitution to Washington. Approval by the United States Congress, President Polk's signature of the annexation act—one by one, the various tangles were being unraveled. Sam Houston chided Jack for his impatience. After all, said the former President, this process was new to mankind's history. Never before had the people of one free nation voluntarily merged themselves within the borders of another. The day would come.

It was February 19, 1845, a gray murky sort of day. The Ranger troop arrived early for the ceremony, to be held in the capitol courtyard in Austin. The only inn in town was crowded to capacity; Major Hays could not have found accommodations if he had desired them. He had not asked, of course. He had camped the night before with his men on the Guadalupe River. They swam their horses across the Colorado. Since the sun didn't come out, Hays awaited the ritual in damp clothes.

Attendance would be meager; Austin had been almost a deserted town these three years. The President's mansion stood empty, its roof leaking. The capitol resembled a barn more than a government house. A company of United States dragoons came marching up the slope, escorting the state's first governor, J. Pinckney Henderson. The Ranger role was to act as guard of honor for Dr. Jones. Jack saw the President start up the hill, and gestured for his troop to dismount. They had never gone through any sort of drill afoot, much less a ceremony of state. They walked in irregular ranks in their assorted garb; ninety-odd of them. Jack felt a little self-conscious in the presence of the nattily uniformed dragoons. What were they thinking—that this was a sorry-looking troop? Were they marveling that such an irregular company could be a nation's entire regular military strength? Well, the Rangers were—and they had been since 1837.

The ceremony was brief. Dr. Jones solemnly proclaimed: "The Republic of Texas is no more." Down fluttered the blue and white flag. The man who had lowered it was uncertain about its disposition. Finally he handed it to Major Hays and Jack took it quickly. He had his own idea about who should receive it: Sam Houston should have the flag for a memento.

Up went The Stars and Stripes. The dragoons saluted smartly and fired a volley in honor of Governor Henderson, then they marched back down the hill and the ceremony broke up in informal talk. Jack's men looked at him expectantly.

He shrugged his shoulders. Perhaps a speech was in order, but he wasn't the one to make it. A nod of his head had made them Rangers in the first place. Let another gesture signify their termination of service.

Jack found lodgings in San Antonio and traded for a lot on King William Street. Here, he had decided, they would live, near the families who had been his closest friends. As yet Susan had not set a wedding date. Stopping by Seguin after the annexation ceremony, Jack had asked for a few weeks to complete his land trades and settle his company's financial accounts. Something over a thousand dollars was due him. Funds were available in Austin to pay him, but the state treasurer was hesitant about signing any such warrant. There were all sorts of complications when a nation suddenly closed up shop.

It was a late April afternoon, almost six o'clock. Jack stepped out of his rooming house to await the Mavericks' carriage. His evening meals were small worry; he received more invitations to dinner than he could possibly accept.

As he stood waiting, a horseman galloping down Presa Street, reined up suddenly, and tumbled to the ground.

"Major Hays?" he demanded. "Well, thank God," he panted when Jack nodded. "The name is Horton, Major. Here—this message is from Governor Henderson. Very urgent. I rode like the devil to get here. Wore out two horses."

Jack unfolded the sheet of paper and the words leaped

up at him. The Comanches were raiding the southwest settlements in force. Governor Henderson had appealed for help to General Zachary Taylor, now stationed at Corpus Christi with three United States regiments. But there was no way of knowing when relief would come from that direction. Without state militia of any sort and only a handful of United States soldiers at his disposal, Henderson could do nothing but appeal to the major. Would Hays gather up volunteers in San Antonio and head off the Indians? Whole villages might be destroyed if he did not.

Jack hurriedly changed out of his dress clothes. After sending an apologetic message to the Mavericks, he went in search of Walker and McCulloch. He had been afraid of this, and so had Governor Henderson and other state leaders. The United States had sent troops to Texas in expectation of Mexican hostility. But nothing had been done at all about protection against the Comanches. That company of dragoons at Austin—it could stand at attention and march in parades, but it would be useless against Indians.

By daylight he had forty volunteers. The Comanche trail was easy to intercept. Yellow Wolf was leading this war party of six hundred warriors. The few victims they had spared repeated the Wolf's guttural boasts: the red men meant to destroy the white settlements, one after another. Wolf, the most famous Comanche war chief, the scourge of the north Plains, was raiding Texas for the first time.

Smoking ruins and charred bodies guided the Rangers toward a small lake at the base of Paint Rock. Jack crept to its summit to study the Indian camp. The Comanches were too strong to attack here, he decided. He led his troop around the mountain range and to the next waterhole, twenty miles from the settlement of Dripping Springs. And only thirty-five miles from Austin, in case the United States government didn't think the Indian threat was serious! No wonder Governor Henderson was alarmed.

Jack stationed his men in scrubby timber around the waterhole. Their accurate fire dazed the Comanches. Yellow Wolf had been told that "Devil Jack" no longer rode the war trails. But here he was, squarely in the Indians' path. The Texans lost no time in letting the savages know whom they faced.

Yellow Wolf had brought these warriors out of the north Plains. They carried bone and flint arrows and spears fourteen feet long. Each brave boasted a shield of thick buffalo hide. And, charging upon the thickets, Wolf made certain the sun shone squarely in the white men's eyes.

The Indians recoiled before the Rangers' steady fire. But Yellow Wolf himself announced that the fight had just begun. He rode close to the brushy cover, haranguing "Devil Jack." The Texans jibed back at his finery. He wore a long buckskin robe fringed with silver ornaments and the naked portions of his body gleamed with war paint. His headdress was the horns of a buffalo. He carried a seven-foot shield.

Yellow Wolf had brooded over the failures of other Comanche war leaders. He believed he had the answer to the white man's superior marksmanship. He divided his warriors into three divisions and they charged at short intervals. Then the three units swung around to attack in unison.

The Rangers had to divide their fire, turning their rifles from one maneuver to check another. Yellow Wolf galloped back and forth between the three divisions, giving each his personal attention. His shield covered him every moment, and his thick buffalo hide protected him from bullets.

"That Wolf," grunted Sam, "is some booger."

Hays nodded. There was no denying Yellow Wolf's clever leadership. The white man's best chance was to strike down the fiery Indian leader. But how? Bullets ricocheted harmlessly off his shield at fifty paces.

Jack slipped to the far edge of the thicket. He lay there with rifle ready, intent on Yellow Wolf. A quick shot might exploit a careless instant. Let Wolf leave himself unguarded—Jack fired at the flash of the chief's nakedness. Wolf had flipped his thick shield; a bullet tore into his exposed side. The Comanche war leader went tumbling backward.

Boldly Hays darted from cover. The Comanches were fanatical about recovering their dead, especially a chief's body. If he could drag Wolf's corpse into the thicket, the savages would go berserk. They would forget any battle strategy. He threw a riata around Wolf's neck as Walker came hurrying to help him. They dragged the dead chieftain into the brush and grimly awaited the inevitable wild rally. It came from all directions, Yellow Wolf's teachings forgotten. Their rifles empty, the Rangers took to their horses. Five-shooters blazing, they met charge with countercharge. For fifteen minutes the Comanches struggled against withering pistol fire; then their ranks broke and the battle turned into a headlong chase across the prairies.

Toward sundown the weary Texans came straggling back to the waterhole. A handsome, stocky man awaited them, Governor Henderson. He had ridden out from Austin to survey the battle scene and make Jack Hays a startling offer.

The governor had finally gotten a sympathetic hearing from President Polk. And events along the Texas border had forced General Zachary Taylor to reverse his stated opinion that the United States Army would be better off without Texan volunteers. The United States now wanted four Texas regiments, including the Rangers. The latter was wanted for immediate duty. And Governor Henderson could offer Jack Hays a colonel's commission in the United States Army!

CHAPTER

10

The Road to Monterrey

Jack Hays heaved a deep sigh. How could he refuse? How could he decline service under the flag he had struggled to raise over Texas? And there were his men to consider— Walker, McCulloch, Wallace, Chevaille, Acklin, all the others. Jack had pitied them these past few weeks. They were at loose ends, waiting for something, but unsure of what it would be. They were frontier fighters by trade and nothing else. They wanted acceptance by the United States Army because they knew nothing else to do. Their feelings went deeper too, much deeper. They wanted to fight Mexico for purely unselfish reasons. The enemy below the Rio Grande was still a personal enemy. Annexation had not changed that. A long, bitter hostility did not melt away because of President's Polk signature and a flag-changing ceremony.

Honor must be considered, and pride. Jack had not tried to make a stand against General Taylor's negative attitude toward the Texan volunteers, but it had rankled. Sure, his regiment cut a poor figure on a parade ground—but they were soldiers. They were fearless and deadly fighters. They had learned a new pattern of warfare, featuring weapons the United States government still scorned. Their pattern would work on this frontier where military strategy would not.

As Taylor had learned in the Texas *monte!* Hays knew full well what had happened. General Taylor had moved his troops to Brownsville on orders of President Polk. Mexico still disputed the Texas claim to the area between the Nueces and Rio Grande. Taylor had sent Captain S. B. Thornton and sixty dragoons to reconnoiter the *brasada.* They had been cut to pieces by Mexican troops under General A. Torrejon. The United States commander was baffled by the terrain ahead. His scouts couldn't even find their own way through the low-lying brush country, much less mark off trails and locate waterholes. Taylor was wise to finally cry "uncle." He could lose every company under his command if he plunged blindly into the *monte.*

Jack discussed the situation with Susan. "I've kept you waiting two years already," he said. "I don't know how long this war will take. General Taylor wants two Texas regiments to enlist for six months. It may be over by then; it may not be."

She looked off. Neither was getting any younger. Her fiancé was twenty-eight and she herself well past the age when Southern girls usually married. But she shook the tears out of her eyes. Who could not appreciate the tremendous pressure on her sweetheart? All of Texas was indignant at the callous attitude of the United States government toward its new acquisition. Particularly did Texans want the Rangers kept in the saddle. Slow-moving regulars with their cumbersome gear could not protect such widely-scattered settlements. Not unless there were thousands of them.

"You must go," said Susan. "I'd hate myself if I didn't insist on it." She forced a happy smile. "So hustle back to

San Antonio and round up your *compadres*. You're itching to get started and you know it. I'll be waiting."

"I don't deserve a woman like you," Jack said slowly.

"Fiddlesticks," she scoffed. "You deserve more out of life than you've gotten. But don't let General Taylor awe you with his dignity and gold braid. You're a better commander any day in the week."

Jack smiled. There was small chance of either him or his followers being awed by military pomp. They had not been sent for until they were needed. And they were needed for their mobility and fighting prowess, and not for their appearance.

A week later, confronting General Taylor, Jack declined uniforms for his regiment.

"Our clothes are fitted for the work ahead," he explained. "We don't like to offer the enemy a good target, so we wear either homespun or buckskin. Both are hard to spot in cover. We can't slip up on a Mexican sentry in cavalry boots. We couldn't ride mustangs using cavalry saddles. No other kind of horses will do us either." He smiled. "We won't be much bother to you, General. Just tell us what you want us to do."

Taylor chewed his mustaches thoughtfully. Two months before, he would have resented this slight young officer's attitude. But the general realized his army's helplessness to deal with the enemy in the southwest terrain. Nothing in his experience had prepared him for warfare in these wild wastes.

"As you wish, Colonel Hays," he said a little stiffly. He had accepted the necessity of enlisting these Texans, but he was not yet reconciled to it. "Our main worry is to find routes we can travel. Since the enemy has attacked us— and blood has been shed on United States soil—there is no question of what we must do. We must advance across the Rio Grande and destroy the enemy's arsenals."

He brought out a makeshift map. "Monterrey is our main objective. I am informed that it is a heavily defended city."

Jack nodded. He was sure that Monterrey was the key bastion of northern Mexico. What was the enemy's potential strength? Hays couldn't answer that. About five thousand Mexican troops had fought in Texas during 1836. Twelve hundred had marched upon San Antonio with Woll in 1842. Surely several times as many could be rallied to the defense of Monterrey.

"Then that's our major campaign," General Taylor decided. "We must move a strong force into attacking position. By what route, Colonel?" He jabbed at the map. "By China or by Camargo?" He leaned back in his camp chair. "Remember, we must move artillery and supplies with us, Colonel Hays. We can't dash lickety-split across mountains and arroyos like your Rangers."

Jack nodded. "No, sir." He studied the map. "The China route is shorter," he said, "but I've never heard of any big military movement along it. You'd better let us cover it first and see." His eyes gleamed as he studied the challenge to his regiment. "We can split up," he mused. "McCulloch and Walker can take one bunch and scout this road." He pointed to the *real* leading through Reynosa and Camargo before reaching Monterrey.

Taylor's eyes flickered. "How could we protect two such scouting expeditions, Colonel?"

"What do you mean, sir?"

"Obviously," Taylor said a little impatiently, "you don't mean to penetrate two hundred miles of enemy country without some support, Colonel."

Jack's eyes danced. "We won't ask for support, General,"

he said. "McCulloch will take one bunch and go this way, and I'll go by China. It'll take some riding, but I reckon we can do it."

The general studied him sternly. "You intend to fight your own way—live off the country—scout both roads to Monterrey—and get back?"

"Yes, sir," Jack said calmly.

Taylor rubbed his chin. "All right," he said with a shrug. "You can try it." He studied the map again. "My plans are to move into position at Reynosa. That's convenient to both routes."

"Yes, sir."

The United States commander gestured that the interview was not over. "You spoke of the mustangs your men ride, Colonel," he said thoughtfully. "I have noticed that these ponies seem better adapted to the terrain. My troops are having trouble with their horses. I've considered requisitioning Washington for several hundred mules. Would they do better in Mexico than our army mounts?"

"Much better," Jack said promptly. "The native mustang is tricky," he added. "A man may think he's used to horses, but he has to learn all over again before he can handle them. My troop's horsemanship isn't an accident. All of my men are carefully picked. A few of them ride mules because they simply don't want to fool with mustangs. I would advise the same for your troopers too. Mules will get you there and back."

"I think so too." The general wrote something in his notebook. "What are the chances of requisitioning mules in this area, Colonel?"

"Very good, sir. Especially in Mexico." Jack's hazel eyes twinkled. "If you like, sir, we'll take on that responsibility too."

"We'll discuss that later," Taylor decided. "It's my idea that you have already bitten off more than you can chew. Cover these routes to Monterrey for us while we are moving to position, and I'll concede your regiment has earned its pay."

But three days later, when Jack led his company into the *pueblo* of San Fernando, he was accompanied by Army Quartermaster Henry Whiting. The United States Army would purchase an unlimited number of mules at twenty dollars per head.

Whiting had offered little objection to Hay's methods until San Fernando was reached. The Rangers had left Matamoras with very little stir and absolutely no ceremony. Jack had divided his regiment and named McCulloch to command the other troop. General Taylor had insisted on reviewing them before their departure. So the Texans had sat their horses impatiently until their colonel had received a final briefing. Then, at his gesture, they had wheeled their mustangs around and ridden off. No camp paraphernalia of any kind was taken, no provisions except what each man carried in his saddlebags or wallet.

A delegation from San Fernando met the Texans outside the *pueblo*. Their *alcalde* acted as spokesman. Quartermaster Whiting listened in amazement at the exchange of Spanish. He managed to decipher the gist of their talk. Instead of resisting the invaders, the town's population begged to be spared.

"The *alcalde* promises to have a hundred mules for you by dark," Jack told Whiting.

The quartermaster frowned. What kind of threats had Colonel Hays delivered?

None especially, Jack shrugged. Texans usually occupied

Mexican towns without opposition. The average native was terrified of the Rangers. The next *pubelo* confirmed his story: it yielded too. Whiting sent another herd of mules back to Taylor's headquarters.

But progress slowed as the Texans turned toward China. This so-called route led along yawning precipices. Often chaparral and prickly pear narrowed the trail so that the Rangers had to ride single-file. Whiting shivered, closed his eyes, and followed after the tireless horsemen.

Certainly this route was impossible for Taylor's army. Hays led his troop to Reynosa, but the general had not yet set up camp in the Mexican town. He was waiting until steamboats proved the Rio Grande navigable to this point. The cautious general had no intention of leaving his supply routes behind.

Ben McCulloch rode in with his weary troops. They'd found the *real* via Camargo usable, but several guerrilla bands had given them trouble. Ben's detail hadn't taken off their boots in four days.

Hays rode downstream to report to Taylor. The general listened appreciatively. Quartermaster Whiting had already prepared him for the Texan officer's report.

"You saved us weeks of time, if not actual losses," the general concluded. "Thanks to you, we have almost enough mules for our purposes too."

"Thank you, sir."

Taylor picked up Jack's report. "I see no mention in here of any skirmishes with guerrillas, Colonel."

"Oh, we had some," Jack said off-handedly. "Captain McCulloch had more than my detail. But it wasn't anything to make a fuss about."

Taylor's manner abruptly changed. "Now," he said

sternly, "let's discuss some of the complaints against your men in Reynosa."

Jack sighed. He had anticipated this difficult scene with General Taylor. It had taken three additional weeks for the first detachment of United States troops to reach Reynosa. During that time the Rangers had held the town themselves. Hays, who had circled off to help Whiting procure more mules, knew that there had been some incidents during his absence. Supposedly, Walker and Chevaille had explained these to General Taylor. Jack struggled to hold back his smile as Taylor read extracts from their reports.

It was not true, Walker had stated, that several unarmed Mexicans had been shot down: "If some of the most notorious of these villains were found shot, or hung up in the brush, we can only assume that in a fit of remorse and desperation, tortured by conscience for the many evil deeds they had committed, they had recklessly laid violent hands on their own lives." Walker also denied that the Rangers had looted Mexican homes to prepare their Fourth of July feast: "A few pigs and chickens were killed accidentally while we were firing salutes in honor of the day."

"I suspect your men of levity too, Colonel," rasped General Taylor. "You must improve discipline if you are to continue as a regular regiment."

Carefully Jack explained: this was Reynosa, where the Mier prisoners had been treated inhumanely. At least a score of his men had suffered indignities from these citizens. His Rangers had long memories; every so often they recognized some of their tormentors of 1842

"As for discipline," Jack concluded, "I could never get the circumspect response you demand of your regulars. My men aren't of that mold, General. They're frontiersmen, independent characters. And idleness doesn't set well with them. My men haven't liked their treatment either. We're still dependent on our resources for subsistence. My recommendation, sir, is that you allow us to take the field. There are a half-dozen guerrilla chieftains ready to heckle your march on Monterrey. Let us clear the road for you."

"I suppose that's the only solution," Taylor said. He hesitated, then added in a different tone, "Don't think I'm unappreciative of what you and your regiment have done, Colonel."

"I understand, General," answered Hays. "We're bad for camp morale. My regiment doesn't drill and my men won't pay lip respect to rank. But we'll do a job for you in the field."

He did not add that he was as impatient for action as his men. He wanted this campaign over with. It galled him to consider that in these three months they had advanced no farther than the Rio Grande. So far the United States Army had accomplished nothing his Ranger troop couldn't have done.

11

A Bastion Falls

The Mexicans considered Monterrey an impregnable position. Probably they were right too—as far as any frontal assault was concerned. But General Taylor, moving carefully into attacking position on September 18, realized the city's weakness. The way into the town was by the Saltillo road. And Taylor was confident that he had the cavalry force to sweep around Monterrey and gain a foothold in the ridges south of the city.

Colonel Hays nodded. He welcomed the assignment. General William J. Worth's Fifth Infantry Division was to move to support the Ranger position. Hays respected Worth's bravery and ability and the Fifth was considered the pick of Taylor's troops.

"Once General Worth has taken his position," ordered the careful Taylor, "you will dismount your companies, Colonel, and support his assaults upon these rear positions."

He gestured to his map. Hays nodded again. The Rangers had established the positions of these Mexican batteries by repeated sallies. Jack had hoped to draw out and destroy a lancer brigade, but Taylor had vetoed the strategy that had worked so well against Woll on the Salado in 1842. He couldn't see men capturing hillside fortifications on mustangs. Hays quietly accepted the general's judgment. Certainly Jack couldn't point to any previous experience in assaulting so strong a bastion. Taylor had proved surprisingly amenable to letting the Rangers fight in their own style against guerrilla forces. Hays led his regiment around the city, intercepted the Saltillo road, held his position despite a dozen small skirmishes. By late afternoon of September 19 the Fifth Infantry had come to their support.

By then the Mexican command had realized the risk of letting the Rangers hold the Saltillo road. Fifteen hundred cavalrymen rode out to regain control of the highway. Jack dismounted five companies. Acklin's men hid in a cornfield with four other companies posted in gullies or behind fences. Every fifth man was sent to the rear with the horses.

McCulloch's company played the decoy, using a ruse gleaned from the Comanches. The center line broke and the overzealous lancers charged right into the full fire of the pincer units.

Worth's arrival with American reinforcements ended the skirmish. In two clashes the Texans had killed 180 men while losing one man themselves. They had clearly established mastery of the terrain before the fortifications. Now what about the Mexican batteries? Artillery from Independence Hill raked them as they considered strategy. What were their chances against Ampudia's fortifications?

Jack waited until the general's inquiring eyes settled full upon him, then answered.

"In my opinion," he said gravely, "we can take the hill. The Rangers can work up the ridge and engage the enemy at close quarters. If the general can bring up his main force in quick support, we'll get them out."

Once before he had led his Texans on such a bold move—against Woll. Then, Caldwell had not moved to support him. He felt that he could depend on General Worth.

Worth assigned Captain F. C. Smith and two hundred regulars to attack with the Texans. Jack quickly designed a battle plan. He sent Chevaille and three hundred Rangers circling back to ford the Santa Catarina several miles downstream.

This movement, he hoped, would draw the full fire of the Mexican batteries. He and the other Rangers, including the army regulars, would plunge straight through corn patches and chaparral and cross the river. The Santa Catarina flowed deep and treacherous here; the Mexicans would not be expecting such a direct assault. In single file the Texans stole through the cane and cornfields. They slipped into the river and fought against its swift current.

Their advance did not go unnoticed. Mexican cannon turned loose upon them. Bullets and grapeshot boiled the water around Hays. But the Texans scrambled up out of the river with small loss and scattered out in the thick chaparral. They stopped briefly to let water drain from their clothes and then stormed the first hilltop battery. Chevaille was drawing his share of attention from the Fort Soldado garrison, while Captain Smith's infantry also took position quickly.

In fact, Smith's regulars were right on the Rangers' heels when they streamed into the abandoned redoubt.

"We almost caught up with you, Colonel," the crestfallen Smith told Hays.

"We'll share it," Jack told him. He took a piece of chalk

from an infantryman and wrote on one of the captured cannon: TEXAS RANGERS AND FIFTH INFANTRY.

He sent a courier to General Worth announcing the capture of the redoubt with two men killed and nine wounded.

The nightly rainstorm came up, but men who had gone thirty-six hours without food or sleep rested anyhow. Long before daylight, however, the Ranger troop was moving again—carrying only side arms, slipping single-file across the boggy cornfields toward Independence Hill. Hays, on his hands and knees in the mud, led his picked followers from one Mexican sentry post to the next. Speaking Spanish softly to allay the suspicions of curious sentries, he engaged their attention while his soft-footed Texans surprised the sentinels from behind. One by one, the Texans captured all of the enemy guards.

Back went the word to Worth to "move up." The Texans started up the sheer bluffs of Independence Hill without waiting for the regulars to overtake them. The Mexicans had believed this eight-hundred-foot height almost invulnerable: the artillery from the Bishop's Palace protected one slope; the other sides were considered unassailable.

The Texans kept climbing in the dark, every man for himself. Loosened stones frequently clattered down the hillside, but a thunderstorm drowned out such sounds. For once Hays was grateful for a blinding rain. No one could see or hear them, and he and his men were climbing "by feel" anyhow. Men shoved and dragged each other up the bluffs and pulled themselves upward by branches.

By dawn they were within a hundred yards of the crest. The startled garrison came alive to the peril and raked the invaders with musket fire. But still the Americans kept climbing. Once at the summit, Rangers and infantrymen cut loose. The first Texan to leap over the fortification's wall of sandbags was Captain Ad Gillespie. He perished there, a stout Ranger to the last, waving his men on with his last gestures.

The Mexicans fought desperately a few moments, but all odds were against them now. Bowies and five-shooters overcame sabers and dress pistols. Finally the garrison pulled itself together for a retreat to the Bishop's Palace, dragging along an artillery piece and two six-pounders.

The Americans held Independence Hill; the enemy occupied the stone fortress across the valley. Two infantry units came up to join the Rangers. Worth proved himself a fighter after Hay's heart. The general was all for moving right ahead. Once the Palace was taken, there would be nothing to stop them from entering Monterrey.

But the stone Palace looked too formidable to storm. At least so Hays decided, and fell back on the battle ruse that had always worked for him and his Rangers. Cannily he put the maneuver into motion again, this time with United States regulars moving as the decoy. A company advanced on the bastion and then fell back in apparent confusion. Out charged the Mexican lancers, with two companies of infantry close behind. The attacking Mexicans found themselves caught between two flanking forces —Walker's on the left, Hays' on the right. When the lancers fell back, their infantry was exposed to the army's counterattack.

Never had Hays' strategy worked better. The Rangers fought their way into the fortress while the battle on the plain still waged hot and heavy. Seizing the guns, the Texans turned cannon upon the Mexicans. They broke under their battering and fled for the shelter of the town.

By mid-afternoon The Stars and Stripes floated over the Bishop's Palace.

The battle now turned to the city itself. Colonel G. T. Wood's regiment of east Texans spearheading Taylor's drive into Monterrey's narrow streets. The American commander was not sure of his own strength; he could not realize how completely the tide of battle had changed in the past twenty-four hours.

The parapets of Monterrey were captured. The last organized resistance was over.

The fighting wasn't though. The Mexicans fought grimly in streets and from housetops. Hays' Rangers stormed down the *Calle de Monterrey*, one of two main streets. The Texans split into groups of five again, with Walker's company concentrating on Mexican sharpshooters lurking on the rooftops.

It was slow, grim business. House by house, the Mexicans were driven back. Every adobe hut was a fortress within itself. screening a handful of desperate defenders. No bullets could penetrate such thick walls; the attackers had to hammer their way in. With crowbars and sledgehammers the Texans pounded against stubborn walls. An opening made, the Rangers lit six-pound shells and blew up the structure.

No weapon was deadlier than the five-shooter at such close range. And every bit of fighting was that: hand-to-hand. McCulloch's riflemen kept the rooftops clear. Often, in that day's hectic fighting, the Rangers were in the lower story of the building while Mexicans held the upper story and roof.

The cease-fire order caught Hays and nine companions in the act of seizing the Hidalgo Hotel. The Texans voiced their resentment of such orders for a few moments, then turned their attention to the problem of food.

At least they had stopped fighting in a good place— a hotel.

An inspection of their prisoners turned up two cooks. The Rangers ordered them to ply their trade *muy pronto,* emphasizing their words with brandished five-shooters. The frightened Mexicans protested that the larder was empty. They couldn't possibly prepare a meal for nine half-starved men. One of the prowling Texans found thirteen sheep fattening in a pen for the hotel's kitchen. These were quickly slaughtered and butchered and the chefs put to work.

The spreading aromas brought more Rangers into the hostelry. The meat supply was sufficient, but no bread was found in the hotel. One of the chefs was handed a dollar and told to return with bread within fifteen minutes or all of his *compadres* would be slaughtered.

He returned so quickly and cheerfully that several Rangers feared the food might be poisoned.

There was a way to find out. The procurer was ordered to eat a slice off every loaf he had brought. He submitted willingly at first, then began protesting as loaf after loaf was sliced for his sampling.

"*Yo senter yo comer no más per semana,*" he protested, meaning that he could eat no more in a week.

But water was handed him to wash down the bread, and ugly five-shooters emphasized the Texans' orders to keep sampling.

When minutes passed without the Mexican's showing any ill effects, the Texans attacked the mutton and bread like wolves. It was their first hearty meal in over forty-eight hours. Their appetites satisfied, the Rangers scattered about the hotel making preparations for sleep.

The weary Hays did not interfere. He selected a room for himself and stretched out on the first bed he had occupied in long weeks. But shortly he was on his feet again, holding off some of his men at pistol point. And not very happily either.

The Mexican officer sent with a white flag to contact the Rangers was the same man who had held the bean jar for the Salado lottery!

Hays finally calmed his aroused followers. It wasn't easy, not with such survivors of the bean drawing as Big Foot Wallace, McCulloch, and Walker threatening to cut out the Mexican's heart. Hays rejected any parley until General Ampudia designated another spokesman.

The next day a Mexican lancer was shot while riding peaceably down the street. Jack heard the noise and hurried to the scene. A five-shooter had killed the native. A dozen Rangers could have done it, but all denied responsibility.

Hays hurried to Taylor's headquarters. He found the general aroused but not unreasonable.

"I realize your predicament, Colonel," said the United States commander. "Your Rangers are rugged individualists. Some of them nurse a bitter hatred for all Mexicans." He shook his head. "But such incidents can't be tolerated, Colonel Hays. I would order your regiment into the field, but your terms of enlistment will expire soon. Besides, I'm not to advance beyond Monterrey without specific orders from Washington."

Hays had heard that rumor. Taylor's army was not to move farther into the interior. Another expeditionary force was forming under General Winfield Scott. This second army would attack Veracruz by sea.

Jack hesitantly voiced the hope he had formed. "If the war is over on this front, General," he proposed, "then let us go home. We're not suited to be occupation troops. My men detest routine." He paused. "I think we've earned a rest," he added.

"Indeed you have, Colonel," Taylor said warmly. "Your regiment has born the brunt of this campaign. All my dispatches to Washington have stated that." He chuckled. "I have eaten my words, Colonel Hays, privately and publicly. I have given full credit to the volunteers I didn't want to take in the first place. For a certain type of maneuver your regiment is fabulous. You'll find yourself a famous man when you return to the United States, Colonel, The American newspapers have printed more stories about your command than the rest of the army put together. I'm happy that we can end our relationship on such a happy note."

"So am I, sir," said Jack, saluting.

Loud hurrahs came from the Rangers as Jack announced their discharge. They would waste little time in leaving either. What was there to do besides mount up and ride north? Walker and McCulloch were ready to leave within an hour.

Colonel Hays called Ben aside to give specific orders. "I'll be here a few more days," Jack explained. "I must settle up accounts and make arrangements to draw our pay. Please call upon Miss Calvert as soon as you get back. Tell her I'll get there as quickly as I can. And suggest to her that she have a wedding date set by the time I arrive."

12

Send Us Hays—*Muy Pronto!*

The spring of 1847 came earlier and more resplendently than usual. At least it seemed so to Jack Hays, getting more and more nervous about the approaching wedding. He wanted it over and done with; so did Susan. Both regretted that they had not set an earlier date. They should have been married immediately upon his return from the Monterrey campaign. But the couple had committed themselves —the two-story residence on South Presa Street was nearing completion—a land trade was working that would give Hays the ranch location he wanted.

Nearly six months had elapsed since release of the Rangers at Monterrey. That had not seemed too long to wait—at the time. Neither Jack nor Susan had anticipated how time would drag. Nor how complications would develop.

Jack's trip to Washington, for example. He hadn't counted on any visit to the national capital. He hadn't expected that President Polk would bolster a personal invitation with orders to complete his regiment's records with the Secretary of War. And what a fuss had been made over the Ranger leader in Washington! Receptions, a dinner, interviews with newspaper corerspondents! General

Taylor had not exaggerated. Texas Ranger exploits had indeed caught the public's fancy. Stories of the daredevil horsemen and their repeating pistols were printed everywhere. Hays could not walk across the street without attracting a crowd.

His visit to Tennessee and Mississippi had been more enjoyable. Sarah had married, and Bobbie was impatient to come to Texas. He was a grown man now, of a less adventurous turn than his brother, but of sturdy character.

"Let me get this wedding out of the way," Jack said, "and my affairs in some order." He shook his head. "They're in quite a mess now. Settling down isn't as easy as you might think."

Newspaper accounts kept him abreast of the war's progress. That war of 1846 was the world's first to be "covered" by firsthand observers. George Wilkins Kendall had set a pattern for other American journalists by sending back dispatches from Zachary Taylor's camp via couriers. So had Jim Freaner of the New Orleans *Delta*. Other periodicals had dispatched correspondents to the front lines. Their stories frequently had been published before the United States War Department had been informed of the battles or skirmishes.

The war was not going too well for the United States. Nowhere did the Mexicans triumph in an organized battle and Americans could gloat over the capture of Veracruz and victory at Buena Vista. But General Taylor's occupation army could not crush such guerrilla chieftains as Generals Urrea and Canales. Frequently these insurgents cut off all communications between Camargo and Taylor's headquarters. Hays had recommended to the Secretary of War that either Sam Walker or Ben McCulloch be commissioned to organize a cavalry regiment to help Taylor.

Regular troops would never overtake guerrillas with their plodding gait.

Returning to San Antonio, Jack learned that Sam had recruited such a company. Hays had to smile at that. General Taylor had thought less of Sam than any other Ranger captain.

Jack's land deal fell through; his twelve thousand acres were still scattered over a wide area. He rode to Seguin to acquaint Susan with this unhappy development. They would have a house to occupy, all right, but he was still without a sure way to support a bride.

Not that he was too worried. His pay as a United States colonel came regularly. He had enough money for current expenses, at least. But, before reining up at the Calvert home, he couldn't help remembering his uncle's disapproval years before. Practical Bob Cage, Jack mused, would be little impressed now by his nephew's business acumen.

"Don't come over here with a sad outlook," scolded Susan. "And, above all, don't dare to suggest any change in our plans. I'll have enough to do to get ready as it is."

Jack smiled, even though he was taken aback by the elaborate preparations his fiancée thought were necessary. "All right," he said. "Just don't expect to play the rich man's wife after the wedding."

"We'll worry about that later," she said with a pert toss of her head. She straightened his tie. "You still don't know how to wear a cravat."

"I haven't had much experience."

"You'll learn," Susan said confidently. "I'm going to make you into a first-class gentleman."

Jack grinned. He had his doubts.

A newspaper correspondent followed him to Seguin; Jim Freaner. Jack received him warmly. Freaner had ac-

companied the Rangers in their assault on Independence
Hill. Here was a journalist willing to face any risk to get
his story.

He had come after a "scoop." Was there any truth to the
rumor that Colonel Hays would lead a Ranger regiment to
General Winfield Scott's relief?

Hays shook his head; Freaner must be thinking about
Walker's regiment and the Monterrey front.

No, the journalist said. A report from Washington had
inspired his hurried trip. Supposedly, President Polk was
dismayed by guerrilla successes against General Scott's
invading force. The Mexican command reportedly had
abandoned any organized resistance against the Americans,
but the natives were redoubling their guerrilla attacks.
Freaner had heard that Scott's troops did not dare leave
camp after nightfall. So many supply trains were being
captured that the American march upon Mexico City was
stymied.

Susan entered the conversation at this point.

"You can write in your newspaper," she said spiritedly,
"that Colonel Hays isn't available for military action at this
time. Certainly General Scott needs him. But my fiancé
has been fighting since eighteen-thirty-six. This is the first
time he has held out of the thick of any battle. He has
earned the right to some personal happiness."

"That he has, Miss Calvert," agreed the journalist. "And
my story in the *Delta* will point that out." He arose, bowed
to Susan, and held out his hand to Jack. "My congratula-
tions and best wishes, Colonel. I hope your happiness is
long and uninterrupted."

"Thank you."

Freaner's eyes twinkled. "But I am still a journalist," he

said. "If you do agree to form another Ranger regiment, will you let me have the exclusive story?"

"I certainly will," promised Jack.

Susan was thoughtful after the journalist's departure. "Am I being too selfish, Jack?" she worried.

"I don't know," he said, "But we've made our plans for this spring. Let's see them through."

"Just why can't other commanders fight off guerrillas?"

"They could," Jack said carefully, "if they would realize the sharp difference between fighting regular troops and fighting mounted guerrillas. We learned that with the Comanches. We couldn't whip them until we could outride them." He hesitated. "The whole thing boils down to this," he added. "This is a whole new country west of the Mississippi. The patterns that worked back there won't pay off in the West. Not in war, anyhow. Or in running a plantation either, if you won't tell your father I said so."

"I won't," she promised. "And I'm inclined to agree. Our crops haven't done as well as expected."

"That's why I'm sort of at loose ends," he said. "I'm not sure what to do about my land. I'll learn, I suppose. It took time to learn about fighting Comanches too."

Her eyes sparkled. "That's the difference between you and the average man," she said proudly. "You reason—plan ahead—train yourself. You'll use new things and study new ideas. You realized what a difference those repeating pistols would make. Other commanders haven't yet."

"The guns made a big difference," Jack agreed. "But don't overlook the horsemanship. We can work in for close-range fighting where regular troops can't." He suddenly grinned. "Now who's changing the subject?" he demanded. "Let's not worry about anything but our wedding. What kind of regalia should I wear?"

The day came at long-last. On the afternoon of April 28, 1847, Jack rode to Seguin with his wedding party. Chevaille and Acklin were to participate in the ceremony; Ben had begged off to accept a captaincy under the beleaguered Taylor. Mrs. Elizabeth Riddle was the only woman in the party. Convention or no convention, she was not going to be left behind. Who, she demanded, had worked harder to marry this couple than she?

At the last moment Susan had to change the scene of the ceremony. So many had responded to invitations that no residence in Seguin could accommodate all who wished to attend. The ceremony room at the Magnolia Hotel was reserved for the ritual.

"Good heavens, Jack," said Chevaille. "You must have invited the whole state."

It seemed so. The population of Seguin had suddenly doubled. Jack Hays nodded glumly. Why hadn't they planned a private wedding? Chevaille turned to look at his friend, a grin splitting the lieutenant's features.

"Jack," he exclaimed, "you're as white as a sheet. You're scared stiff, aren't you?"

The trembling Hays did not deny it. "No battle was ever like this," he sighed, fussing with his collar. "Is my tie straight, Kit?"

"It's *bueno*," grinned Acklin. "Cheer up, *amigo*. No groom ever died at his wedding yet."

"This one isn't over yet," groaned Jack.

But he managed to meet the ordeal. He stood with Susan before a Presbyterian pastor with banks of flowers all around them. He had to close his eyes to keep from staring at his bride. In her mother's wedding gown she was easily the most beautiful bride Jack had ever seen.

Finally it was over. But another trying task lay ahead. At least half of the crowd rode with the newly married couple toward San Antonio. When they reached the Salado River, they found dozens of well-wishers awaiting them with picnic baskets. Ladies had come out from San Antonio in fourteen carriages to welcome Jack Hays' wife.

Then, nearing San Antonio, a newly organized regiment of home volunteers took over. The newlyweds were escorted to the Alamo and rifles were raised, cannon thundered, bells rang out. To Jack's protestations about the lavish ceremony Samuel Maverick said gently:

"This is San Antonio, Jack. We remember eighteen-forty-two."

Then, at last, the couple were alone in their new home.

Two glorious weeks later Governor Henderson rode up with a mounted escort. Their friendship had strengthened during the Monterrey campaign. No man to sit in his state capital while war waged, Henderson had taken leave of his duties to command an infantry regiment. For a while the two men talked of the Monterrey battle. Henderson believed, as did most Texans, that Zachary Taylor had accepted surrender too quickly. Another day's action would have brought unconditional capitulation of the city.

Susan served tea and cakes to the governor's entire party, lingered with the gentlemen for a short while, then departed discreetly. Henderson withheld serious business until he was alone with Hays.

"Well, Jack," he said with a shrug, "I'm sure you know what I'm here for."

"I can guess," Hays answered. He had read recent copies of the New Orleans and Washington newspapers. The editors of these journals were disgusted with the war's progress and demanded that the President take action to end the stalemate between Veracruz and Mexico City.

"President Polk asked me to intercede with you," explained the governor. "He wants another regiment of mounted volunteers. He has asked that you organize it and move to Scott's support at once."

"That won't be so simple," Hays reflected. Chevaille had already gone off to serve as McCulloch's lieutenant. Jack doubted if he could find a dozen men in San Antonio with their own five-shooters.

Henderson smiled at this observation. "So Polk knows," he said. "I told him that the United States government would have to procure more repeating revolvers. He contacted your old friend, Samuel Colt."

"But he hasn't been manufacturing any weapons. At least I'd heard he was out of business."

The governor nodded. "Yes, but he is back in operation. His first order from the United States was for a thousand revolvers to equip this new regiment. You'll be interested in his new design, Colonel. His latest model has six cylinders instead of five."

Jack quickly nodded. There was no reason why the extra cylinder should slow the gun's action. And it would give each man one more shot per gun.

"Will you take the commission, Jack?" asked Henderson. "The President is anxious to know. He has ordered General Scott to hold his positions until he has mounted reinforcements."

"I'll discuss it with my wife," promised Hays.

Susan had already prepared herself for his leaving. "You must go," she said softly. "I'm just grateful that we had these two weeks."

"So am I," said Jack. "And they're just the beginning." He sighed. "I suppose you're weary of hearing it," he added, "but I don't intend to spend the rest of my life campaigning."

13

Exit Santa Anna—Without Applause

Five weeks later Hays fretted over the shortcomings of his newest command. Only about fifty of these five hundred volunteers had previous experience with the Rangers. The others must learn from scratch about handling six-shooters and maneuvering as a troop. They were good horsemen, however. Despite their hurried recruitment, Hays had selected only volunteers accustomed to nimble, spirited mustangs.

The lack of experienced officers hampered him at first, but finally he wangled a transfer for Chevaille. His other captain, Jacob Roberts, showed quick promise. Major E. M. Truett's main responsibility was to handle the myriad of details which the United States Army required of a regimental commander. These duties were not for Hays—he was a field leader, not a desk martinet.

They traveled by ship from Port Isabel. Their mustangs, following by slower transport, reached Veracruz a week later. Another few days were lost awaiting the arrival of Samuel Colt's six-shooters. Finally the impatient colonel had his men mounted and armed for drill.

The next obstacle to be overcome was the swarm of curious spectators. Let a United States trooper have a leisure

moment and he wandered over to watch the Rangers perform. Never had these blue-clad men seen such drilling.
Nearly five hundred men galloping their horses at break-
neck speed, suddenly reining up and spraying targets with
pistol shots! The revolvers were not used from prone or
standing positions. That kind of shooting called for rifles,
with twice the range and accuracy of pistols. These Texans
didn't have to be taught that variety of marksmanship. But
all needed schooling in the six-gun: how to use it and
when. The repeating revolvers were for close-hand combat,
for a sudden countercharge, to gun down a fleeing foe. Two
things made them unbeatable soldiers, lectured their colonel. Their horsemanship gained them advantage of position; their superior fire-power overwhelmed their enemy.

"There's no question of your fire-power, Colonel," said
Major General Robert Patterson after watching a Ranger
drill. "For the kind of battles you fight—quick, unexpected
skirmishes—you have the fire-power of three or four thousand regulars."

Hays nodded, pleased that such a high-ranking officer
understood his regiment's strategy. He had always felt that
General Taylor had accepted Texan aid without bothering
to analyze their real strength—or to realize their inade-
quacies either.

General Patterson was not immune to guerrilla trouble
even in the small zone he commanded: Veracruz and vicinity. Hays asked permission to send Captain Roberts in pursuit of troublemakers. He wanted to see how his new leader
performed in the field.

Patterson agreed, and off rode Roberts' troop. Jack nervously awaited their return. "This will show," he wrote
Susan, "how much these recruits have learned since reach-

ing Mexico." The report was gratifying, especially Roberts' attitude.

"Had a little ruckus on the Medellin River," the captain said tersely. "Nothing to it. Jumped this bunch of guerrillas. Chased 'em a spell but lost 'em in the mountains."

"What casualties?" asked the conscientious Truett, determined to do a good job with his formal reports.

"None for us," said Roberts. "For them—oh, I don't know. Put down five or six."

"Five?" questioned Truett. "They must not have made any sort of a stand."

"Yep, they did," admitted Roberts. He scratched his head. "Make that twenty-five," he said.

Colonel Hays had to turn away to hide his smile. He had made no mistake in his choice of captain! Roberts would continue the tradition of Walker and McCulloch.

Jack reported to General Patterson that his company was ready to move up. Every dispatch from Winfield Scott's headquarters had urged the Rangers to report as soon as possible. The American army had captured the capital without too much opposition. But the war wasn't over by any means. Santa Anna had fled into the mountains. A dozen guerilla bands remained fiercely loyal to him.

"I reckon we are as ready as we'll ever be, General," Hays said.

"Very well, Colonel," agreed Patterson. "I'll give orders for your escort to get ready."

"Our what?"

"Your protection," said the general. "My orders are to detach two field regiments for escort." He smiled a little indulgently at Jack's expression. "It's a long march to Mexico City, Colonel. Some of it is wild country. We've covered it once, but we haven't subdued the territory by any means. The natives fell away from our advance, then reformed behind us."

"Yes, sir," agreed Hays. He knew that guerrillas had re-established headquarters at Jalapa, Puebla, and Atlixo. His regiment could expect battle at all three places and probably points in between. "We're here to fight guerrillas, General," he said slowly. "It makes no difference to us when and how we do it. We'd just as soon fight our way into Mexico City. It's the same thing."

"Well," considered Patterson, "it's your place to refuse escorting troops if you like."

"We'll get there," Jack promised.

Thirty days later he led his regiment into Mexico's capital. Word had swept ahead of their coming. Three quick, decisive victories over guerrillas had raised excitement over the Texans' approach. But it was a disappointing entrance to anyone wanting to make an occasion of it. There was nothing impressive about a formless group of horsemen riding along together.

Jack kept from showing his excitement, and his followers managed to match his impassiveness. It wasn't easy. This was Mexico City, Santa Anna's stronghold. The order of events at San Antonio, San Felipe de Austin, and Harrisburg were sharply reversed. So were the circumstances under which another group of Texans had reached Mexico City—in 1843. Then Walker, McCulloch, Wallace, Acklin—nearly two hundred of them—had been paraded in chains.

Word flew along the streets. *Los diablos tejanos!* The cry swept from lip to lip as Mexico City's populace packed the cobblestone avenues to watch. Hays appraised the forming crowds and gestured for his men to keep alert. It was an unnecessary command. The tenser these Rangers, the more loosely they sat their saddles.

Suddenly a stone sailed through the air, striking a Texan's shoulder. He spotted his assailant in the act of throwing, his six-shooter leaped from its leather holster, and a *metizo* fell dead.

Hays' lips tightened, but he acted as if he had seen and heard nothing.

Further on, another stone was hurled. Another dead Mexican! The resentful mob followed the Rangers to the Grand Central Plaza, encircled them as Hays dismounted. He studied the crowd a moment, then shrugged his shoulders and entered Scott's headquarters. As he stood giving his identity to Scott's orderly, still a third stone was thrown. Several six-shooters barked at once. The panic-stricken crowd hurriedly scattered.

Hays turned to find General Scott frowning at him.

"What kind of an entrance is this, Colonel?" demanded the American commander.

"The kind we had to make, sir," Jack said evenly. "We don't intend to be pelted with stones."

He had tried to mollify General Taylor about his men's behavior and had not succeeded. He did not intend to repeat the futile effort. General Scott had sent for the Rangers because they were quick with their repeating pistols. Well, here they were.

"I suppose some sort of incident was unavoidable," considered Scott. "Your men must protect themselves, of course. But I hope we can hold these demonstrations to a minimum."

Jack nodded. He hoped so too, but he didn't promise it. That night one of his Rangers was beaten to death by a

small mob. The victim, Adams Allsens, lived long enough
to describe his assailants. The next morning eighty bullet-
riddled natives were found near the scene of assault. Colonel Hays truthfully denied any knowledge of the shoot-
ings. Nor did he volunteer his prediction that the Rangers
could walk the streets safely from then on. He only struggled to hold back his smile when General Scott made short
shrift of military complications. The Rangers were ordered
out of the capital and into action with minimum of delay.

Otumba—San Juan Teotihucan—puebla Oaxaca. Hays
barely mentioned these places in his letters to Susan. His
reports to General Scott were not much more elaborate. He
noted the defeat of Juarata, a fanatical *padre* who had organized some five hundred followers into a formidable
force. Hays expressed confidence two weeks later that
United States wagon trains could move safely along the
Veracruz-Mexico road. An American division under General Joseph Lane set up occupation units in the Rangers'
wake. "Colonel," groaned Lane, "We can't occupy towns
as fast as you take them."

Hays agreed. Of course not. It wasn't necessary in any
case. The guerrilla chieftains no longer elected to defend
their towns. Their style of resistance baffled the regular
soldiers—but not Rangers. Texans with their six-shooters
climbed rooftops after snipers. They battered through
adobe walls to wipe out nests of sharpshooters. The enemy
took to the hills for safety. Even there they were outridden
as well as outfought. Equal weapons might have turned the
tide against this regiment of invaders. But brave and stubborn men could not take up *escopetas* and stand off the
combination of rifles and six-shooters.

How long would this sort of warfare last? Every Texan

knew the answer, and most United States commanders came to believe it. Until Santa Anna was captured—that was how long. He was their real quarry; these guerrilla chieftains were just additional trouble in their tireless pursuit. The United States high command finally let Walker and McCulloch scourge out of Monterrey. The net grew tighter with each Ranger triumph. Somewhere in these mountains Santa Anna maintained a secret headquarters. From there, via couriers, streamed out the dictator's orders —and also the inspiration that fanned these fires of resistance.

A captured Mexican near Tehuacán provided the first real clue as to Santa Anna's hideout. He was a personage of obvious importance with a safe-conduct signed by General P. F. Smith. But some of his answers were vague and Hays confided his suspicions to Chevaille.

"Mike," he said, "I know where this bird has been."

"Tehuacán," said Chevaille. "He said so."

"And at Tehuacán," said Jack, "he got orders from Santa Anna."

Mike's eyes widened. "Are you just guessing?"

"Mostly," Jack admitted. "But let's play that hunch."

He released the prisoner, threatening physical harm if the carriage did not continue on to Oaxaca. Then the Rangers started toward Tehuacán. They traveled all night, reaching the town at daylight. Everywhere were signs of wild and hasty flight. A search of the *pueblo's* most pretentious house confirmed Jack's suspicions: Santa Anna had been quartered there. The long dining table had not been cleared. Seventeen abandoned trunks were found in an adjoining room.

Tehuacán's frightened *alcalde* revealed how near the Rangers had come to capturing the dictator. A courier just after midnight had warned Santa Anna that Brigadier General Lane was approaching with an American brigade. It had been a false report, but the dictator had fled in time to avoid an enemy approaching from the opposite direction.

Lane took charge of the *pueblo*, stationing a garrison there. The spoils found in Santa Anna's abandoned headquarters were forwarded to the dictator's wife, except for some personal effects. Hays drew a personal trophy—a cane embossed with gold, diamond, rubies, and other precious jewels.

He handed it to General Lane. "Send it to President Polk with my compliments," he said.

The trail led to Orizaba. The Rangers crossed a mountain range near the snow line at an altitude higher than fifteen thousand feet. The horses staggered along at a slow walk. Men bled at the nose.

Their bird had flown, leaving a garrison of two thousand soldiers and a battery of several brass cannon to stand off the Texans. They didn't. Their *alcalde* surrendered on Hay's promise not to raze the town. The impatient Rangers had to await Lane's arrival. This was too important a military point to leave ungarrisoned.

On went the chase. At San Juan Teotihucan the Rangers captured the stronghold of Colonel Manuel Falcón, the guerrilla leader who had been dodging Sam Walker's pursuers. Hays turned south before meeting his former lieutenant and they rode seventy-five miles to attack Tulancingo at daybreak. They crushed another guerrilla troop at Sequalteplan, killing thirty, capturing several. In fourteen days they had covered five hundred miles. There was no telling how many men they had killed.

Into Jalapa they rode, adding a dramatic flourish to their entrance. Each Ranger carried a captured lance and some of the banners they had seized. The *alcalde* begged for leniency and the Texan colonel nodded. His men were tired; they would rest here.

Before the next day Lane's hard riding couriers overtook them. General Winfield Scott ordered an immediate cessation of hostilities. Santa Anna had decided to throw himself upon the mercies of the United States commander. Somehow the dictator had slipped by the Rangers and surrendered to Scott in person. The general had lost no time in granting the deposed dictator permision to leave the country with his entourage.

Santa Anna's party would pass through Jalapa. General Scott ordered Colonel Hays and his regiment to ensure the dictator's safe passage.

The orders fluttered from Jack's fingers. Mike scooped them and digested their contents at a glance.

Safe-conduct for Santa Anna! The Ranger captain almost choked in his fury.

But Hays performed his duty. He politely presented his respects as the dictator's entourage approached Jalapa. Santa Anna seemed in high spirits. He was chatting amiably with other American officers when Colonel Hays was presented. The dictator's face paled and his eyes burned. He looked off without saying a word.

Hays bowed and rode back to his Rangers, who were drawn up along Santa Anna's route.

"Get set," he warned Roberts and Chevaille. "Santa Anna will be along any minute."

"Did you see him?"

Jack smiled. "I was presented to him," he said drily.

"What did he do?"

"He did nothing. He said nothing. He didn't seem glad to meet me."

Chevaille grunted. "What about us?" He gestured to the two rows of Rangers. "I reckon they'll hold quiet," he said grimly. "Reckon we can make 'em. But they won't stand at attention or any of that fancy stuff."

"They don't have to," Hays said firmly. "We'll let Santa Anna pass, but we won't bow and scrape before him. We never did."

The procession came into sight. Most of the Texans leaned against stone fences on either side of the road. All of them were afoot. Not a man stirred as the big gilded carriage pulled abreast. The drivers, however, made the ordeal a brief one. They cracked whips and forced the four prancing horses into a hurried gallop.

Hays stared thoughtfully after the dictator. That settling cloud of dust meant the end of the war. A long war too—for him. When had it bugun? It wasn't easy to remember. Almost eleven years before. For in the spring of 1836 he had splashed his horse across the Sabine River and followed a dirt road to Nacogdoches. He shook his head and turned to his horse. His path lay in the opposite direction from the last ceremony of this war. Maybe, he mused, that was a good omen.

Now to prove to a certain young lady that he was finished as a soldier.

14

The Apaches Refuse to Parley

Hays tactfully broached the idea to Susan. She was shocked. Leave Texas to seek a new life in California! She hadn't considered that possibility for a moment. When had such a bee begun stirring in his bonnet?

"On the way home," Jack said. He explained further. The Ranger regiment had returned by steamer, *The Maria Burt*. There had been nothing else to do but stare out over the blue water and mull over peaceful ambitions. Slowly his plan took shape. He wanted to make a complete break with his Texas circumstances. A fresh start, he was sure, would be easier in a new country. That was his heritage—to look West for the place to begin over again.

Susan could not deny some advantages of a move. In four months her husband had done little about improving his financial position. Distractions kept coming from all sides. He had been summoned to Washington to settle his regiment's accounts. Almost daily he was asked to supplement earlier survey notes on land locations. The claims of former soldiers for back due wages kept him writing letters to Austin or Washington.

Offers came, yes. Susan had held her breath until her husband firmly rejected the first opportunity. She had feared that appointment as a brigadier general in the United States Army would be too tempting. Hays said no. The next proposal for his future excited Susan. An Austin group announced plans to project Colonel Hays as a gubernatorial candidate. Other pledges of support quickly reached the house on South Presa Street. But Hays shook his head. As Sam Houston had said, he had no bent for politics. He rode to Austin to silence such speculation. His way lay him through a new county organized earlier that year—Hays County. The few citizens of San Marcos paid little attention to the lone horseman plodding past the cluster of business houses. The soldier for whom the county was named went unrecognized in the county seat.

California! Sam Houston's visit to San Antonio spurred Jack's scheming. Senator Houston pointed to his own experiences.

"At your age I was even more of a confused, uncertain figure," he said. "I had to come into a new country to find myself. If you don't want to be governor—or congressman —then California might offer the answer. Certainly you can avoid out there the pitfalls of fate that hold you prisoner here."

The Senator had brought another United States offer for Hays to consider. The Department of Interior was studying establishment on an Indian reservation somewhere along the Gila River. Little was known about that region or the Indians who inhabited it. An exploring expedition would be necessary. Why not kill two birds with one stone? asked Houston. Hays could perform still another service for his government and at the same time solve his financial worries momentarily. Let the United States government equip his party for the California journey. If he reported a reservation for the Apaches practical, then he could consider next if he wished to serve as agent. Certainly he could get the appointment if he wanted it.

Hays nodded. He had been worried about outfitting a party for the long overland march.

Susan accepted his decision in good spirits. "We won't be separated too long," she said bravely. "And I do realize one thing: there's no quiet life for you in Texas. People have grown so dependent on you. You're the first man they think of in an emergency."

A cholera epidemic delayed the expedition's start. Jack took Susan away from town to a camp on the Medina River. Better some privations, he reasoned, than exposure to the town's contamination. She fell ill anyhow—but of influenza not the dreaded cholera. Still, Hays refused to leave until she had fully recovered.

Texas newspapers proudly acclaimed the expedition. The flood of migrants to the California gold camps was reaching great proportions. Texas wanted its share of their traffic. "The intrepid Colonel Hays," wrote one editorialist, "will blaze a southern route to the new country. Thousands will follow after him. The entire nation will soon realize that the most convenient approach to the Gold Coast is via steamer to a Texas port, then along the Hays Trail through the deserts."

Inquiries came every day asking if Hays would accept other migrant parties under his protection. He rejected each request. His route was uncertain. He must turn aside from any sort of trail to contact Indian tribes along the Gila. United States troopers would accompany the explorers as far as El Paso, but the Hays party must face the desert's dangers alone. All volunteers were carefully screened. Thomas B. Eastland was accepted, and John B. Caperton, a young soldier eager to reach the new frontier.

Almost at the last minute arrived a welcome recruit from Mississippi. Bob Hays had decided not to wait any longer.

A month later Hays waited near El Paso del Norte for an enigmatic white chieftain of the Apaches, John Gordon.

A former Ranger, John Glanton, had offered to contact the renegade. Glanton had become a scalp hunter for the Mexican authorities. The tricks of Indian fighting learned against the Comanches had stood him well in his grisly trade. He'd collected handsome bounties for dead Apaches.

The Apaches were the ones to make peace with or subdue, said Glanton. Other Indian tribes such as the Yumas and Diggers would not molest the white man's caravans. But a pact with the Apaches—Glanton doubted it. Had any white man ever smoked peace pipes with the Comanches? Glanton reckoned the desert Indians as fierce and as formidable as the prairie savages.

Who was John Gordon? Hays relayed the scattered bits of information back to Washington. Nobody was sure, except that Gordon was a white man and that he led the Apaches in unrelenting warfare against Mexican soldiers.

One evening Gordon rode casually up to the Coontz Ranch and presented himself to Hays. He was a thick-set young man with bright blue eyes and blond hair. And quite willing to explain his baffling role in Apache affairs.

He was an Englishman who had deserted his ship at an American port. Coming west as an enlisted man in Colonel A. W. Doniphan's regiment, he had deserted after killing a civilian in El Paso. He made no boast of his position among the savages, but Hays had learned that from other sources. This soft-spoken white man was their most notorious war leader. Less than a month before, he had led an attack upon a squadron of United States dragoons near Dona Ana.

Gordon minced no words about his loyalty to his adopted people. He personally deplored their hostility toward the Americans. But he doubted if his savage cohorts could be persuaded to accept any sort of treaty.

He would call them into council, he finally said. Let Hays' party meet him at the peak called El Piancho. Gordon would urge his red brothers to leave off their war against the Americans. The United States government's idea of a reservation—the Englishman chuckled. He would not dare propose such a wild scheme to an Apache war council!

Hays agreed, having decided himself that a reservation was impossible. He had written Susan that his business on the Gila was nearly over. Autumn should find him in California surveying prospects for an occupation and a home.

Three days dragged by after the Americans reached the desert peak. Finally Gordon appeared, alone again. Hays smiled as the Englishman walked toward him. Gordon's armament was mindful of the earlier Ranger company. The Englishman carried a heavy rifle, Colt revolver, a long dagger-shaped knife, and wore an eagle feather in his battered hat.

Only the Gila Apaches were willing to parley, he said. The other desert clans refused to have any dealings with the white man. If Hays wanted to meet with the Gilas, their council would come to a rendezvous at a peak some eighty miles away.

"There is no hope of persuading the other clans to take part?"

Gordon gestured with both hands. "No. Why should

they?" he asked in the next breath. "Men like Glanton have done great harm. The only Gringos the Apaches know about are killers hired by Mexico. Why should they believe you are any different?"

Hays nodded. He had expected to find that attitude.

"But the Gilas will parley?"

"Yes. They have shown that much trust in me. I hope I can convince them to accept your terms."

The meeting place was Ben Moore's Peak, according to the maps Hays carried. Philip Cook had circled near it on an earlier march and had designated the rugged height as a landmark. Hays and his party moved slowly toward it.

Gordon was never far away; Hays saw his smoke signals every late afternoon. But no Gila Apaches arrived to parley. Finally Hays took Caperton and scaled the peak. From its crest they saw why no Indians had appeared for the scheduled peace conference. Far below them waged a running fight between two mounted forces. Riding down to investigate, Hays found that a troop of Mexican cavalry from Ures had routed the Gila party.

They'd taken heavy toll too. The Mexicans boasted nine sets of ears.

General Jose Maria Elias voiced his regrets when he learned that his cavalry had interrupted a parley. But he could not be too apologetic: his troopers had rescued four girl prisoners. Grimly he showed Hays how the captives had been mistreated. The girls were little more than idiots now.

Hays returned to camp and awaited word from Gordon.

The Englishman came early the next morning. The Gilas had fled back to their mountain hideouts, he said. He doubted if they could ever be persuaded that they had not been led into a trap. He had lost considerable favor with them. The Apaches considered that he had showed lamentable weakness as a leader.

"But we knew nothing of the attack," protested Hays. "There's no coordination between Mexican and United States troop movements."

Gordon nodded. He knew that, but the Apaches didn't. "In their eyes, Colonel," said the Englishman, "your people and the Mexicans are common enemies. Your countrymen who have taken service with the Mexicans are responsible for that. And after yesterday. . . ."

He shook his blond head. "There is no peace possible, Colonel," he said slowly. "And I have no choice but to make my own part clear. I am an Apache."

"Which means?"

"I fight with them," Gordon said tersely. His eyes avoided Jack's. "You have a long way to travel, Colonel," he added. "I advise that you get your party moving at once. Right now the Gilas are licking their wounds. But who knows how they will feel about you in a day or two?"

Hays nodded. "If they decide to attack us," he said a little grimly, "I advise you to take no part."

Gordon's eyes flashed. "If they must attack," he said, "I will lead it. Good-by, Colonel Hays."

He turned and strode to his horse.

Hays gave orders to break camp immediately. There was no point in taking Gordon's warning lightly. Straight ahead were the Chiracahua Mountains; Hays guided his party toward them. Sentinels rode the flanks and a guard watched for any rear attack. After dark the livestock were brought inside the circle of wagons. On past the Chiracahua ridges and into the Playa de las Palmas. The ravines and precipitous hills offered obstacles the average migrant never dreamed of overcoming. Often the wagons were pulled up by lariats and inched down bluffs the same way. Bitter cold tortured the travelers at night. They slept fitfully, close to the fires.

Then they were out of the mountains and into the second tier of deserts. Many travelers had found this last lap of the journey the most perilous. Everywhere along the bleak route they found pitiful signs of faltering human progress—skeletons of oxen and horses, discarded furniture, and abandoned wagons. They moved at night to avoid the heat, and nursed their horses and mules on stalks of cottonwood. The Yuma Indians traded mesquite beans and dried pumpkin seeds for powder, and also helped the travelers swim their tired mounts across the Colorado River. Even in autumn, Hays' party almost failed. They threaded their way past Warner's Ranch to the abandoned mission at San Diego, and finally to the town itself. For the last three days of their march they had only green olives to eat.

From San Diego, Hays mailed his report about the Apaches. He "deemed it folly to affect any good with these Indians."

A week later he wrote Susan that he was fascinated with San Francisco. He'd arrived on January 25, 1849. Such a scene he had never seen before. Thousands of impatient men wading through mud deeper than their ankles. A sprawling city with few sidewalks. Saloons and gambling houses everywhere. A fabulous place, but not as fantastic as the prices. A pair of knee-length rubber boots cost 150 dollars. Lodging in a plain room with eight other men cost him three dollars per night. Supper was two dollars.

"The sooner we get to the gold fields," grumbled Caperton, "the better. A man has to own a gold mine to live in this town."

Hays could not deny that. A man had to change his ideas about money. It flowed in streams in this boom city, especially at the gambling casinos. Hays and young Caperton visited these out of curiosity, not to play. Their scant funds would not have carried them through even a small run of bad luck.

The gold fields lay farther inland; those who could afford it traveled from Frisco by river steamer. Hays inquired about passage to Sacramento. All reservations were taken, he was told.

"But we may have cancellations, Colonel Hays," said the clerk. "Shall I get in touch with you if there's a vacancy?"

Jack nodded and gave the address of the rooming house where tenants sat around a single sheet-iron stove. As they walked back up Market Street he suddenly remembered something.

"That agent called me Colonel Hays—as if he had heard of me."

Caperton chuckled. "He has, Colonel. Most people in California have."

John Caperton spoke truthfully. The next day Hays was approached by men he had never seen before who introduced themselves and offered to buy him drinks. Others pressed invitations upon him. And, before he could get steamer transportation to Sacramento, a party of San Francisco merchants called upon him at his rooming place. Samuel Brannan and George B. Reed spoke for them.

"We won't waste time, Colonel," Brannan said briskly after an exchange of introductions. "We learned three days ago that you were coming to Frisco. We haven't wasted much time since then. We represent a number of merchants and investors in the city. We want you to be our candidate for sheriff."

Jack was speechless.

"Gentlemen," he finally managed to protest, "you must be joking. I haven't decided on locating in San Francisco yet."

Brannan nodded. "So we heard. That's why we wasted no time putting our cards on the table. San Francisco is on its way to becoming a hell hole, Colonel. There are two candidates for sheriff, and I wouldn't trust either any farther than I could throw a bull by the tail. Both are involved with shady factions. It takes a new, new broom to sweep clean. And you've brought a good reputation for clean-sweeping from Texas."

Hays smiled. He liked Brannan instantly. The merchant's straightforward manner reminded him of his Texas associates.

"I appreciate the honor, gentlemen," Jack said slowly, "but I can't give your proposition serious consideration. I came to California looking for financial opportunity, not a political career. I have always shunned politics."

"So we know," agreed Reed. "You could have been governor of Texas. That's what we want most in a sheriff —a man who isn't a politician."

"And don't fret about finances," Brannan said. "The office of sheriff pays well. The way the city is growing, you should net twenty thousand dollars a year from the office. You could use the job to get yourself established, Colonel. It'll support you while you survey the area and choose an occupation. Or property to buy."

Jack smiled again. "You speak as if I could win any

election. Gentlemen, I'm no candidate. I never made a speech in my life, nor asked for a man's vote."

"True," nodded Brannan. He rose to leave. "Well, think it over, Colonel. Ask anybody in San Francisco about Sam Brannan. I've fought for law and order since this rush started. I'm up to my ears in city politics as well as county voting. I've made my pile; I don't ask a thing for myself. I want San Francisco to grow great and grow clean. We need a man of your caliber for sheriff. You have a reputation already. You're——"

"I don't understand that," interrupted Hays. "How could I have a reputation in California?"

"It flew ahead of you," said the merchant with a smile. "You're Jack Hays of the Texas Rangers. You'll run a good race, Colonel. You might win, if the honest, law-abiding people get in behind you. I won't tell you it's a cinch. These gamblers won't give up easily. They'll fight you tooth and toenail. But I don't reckon that scares you. You're used to fighting."

"Yes," admitted Hays.

"Well, think it over," Brannan said again. "We'll get together a group for dinner tonight. You can meet some of our friends and make your own decision."

"I'll accept the dinner invitation," Jack said ruefully. "I can't do anything else—the way meals cost out here."

15

Sheriff on Horseback

Jack listened attentively to the San Francisco businessmen. There was no doubting their sincerity or their determination. They wanted a candidate who could defeat "Colonel" J. J. Bryant for sheriff. Bryant operated the Exchange Casino and personally ran the biggest faro game in town. Already the gamblers wielded great influence in the city's government. Bryant's election would ensure their control of the county organization as well.

"You won't lose by it, Colonel," Sam Brannan promised several times. "We'll put up the expenses of your campaign. If we can't elect you, then we'll help you get started in business. You needn't go to Sacramento and the gold fields looking for opportunity: San Francisco has everything to offer. Or will have if we ever get rid of these hoodlums."

Hays was convinced of San Francisco's great future. The only sea outlet for an area including the fabulous gold country—of course, the city would grow. And the prospect of serving as the Gold Coast's first sheriff appealed to him. The fees of the office would get him off to a sound financial start, for one thing. This was not service for a meager stipend such as the Rangers had given.

"I'm considering your proposition, gentlemen," Jack told Brannan's group. "Just give me a little while longer to decide."

Young John Caperton was convinced already. San Francisco needed a sheriff of Jack Hays' caliber. The city reeked of crime. One lawless clan called itself "The Hounds." These were men who had come to California as volunteers in 1846. Theirs was still a military type of organization. But instead of furthering law and order, they preyed upon Spanish and Negro peoples. In some respects "The Hounds" were as evil as the dreaded "Sydney Ducks." These were ruffians from Australia and escaped convicts from British penal settlements in the Pacific who concentrated along the waterfront, the "Barbary Coast." No citizen was safe near the wharves.

Both situations challenged Hays. He had defended Mexican minorities in Texas more than once. And these hell holes along the bay shore! Wouldn't he like to take a few Rangers and invade some of those dives? How long would these tough Australians defy six-shooters and bowie knives?

He agreed to the race. He'd run for sheriff, he told Brannan's committee. But let his supporters understand one thing: If elected, he was through with politics. These civic-minded men claimed they wanted no spoils of office. Well, let them be doubly sure—there would be none handed out!

Brannan chuckled. More than ever, he declared, they were convinced they had chosen the right candidate.

Now to elect him. Brannan insisted on a parade to announce Hays' candidacy. Jack consented to ride down Market Street with a band. A wagon covered with banners and drawn by four horses carried musicians and candidate.

Bryant answered this new challenge by engaging bands around the clock. The gambler bought lavish advertisements in the San Francisco newspapers. He dispensed free drinks from his saloon. On the day of election he had Portsmouth Square encircled with his bands and barkers.

The first return showed Bryant leading. Samuel Brannan called a hurried conference. Something must be done, worried the merchant. What kind of a stunt would offset Bryant's extravagant show?

Hays vetoed several suggestions, feeling that he had taken part in too many undignified demonstration as it was.

"I'll put on one kind of a show, gentlemen," he said. "I have only my honesty to offer and my acquired skills with pistols and a horse. I'll demonstrate those for everybody to see. Maybe my kind of a show won't make much of an impression, but let's try it anyhow."

Brannan helped him procure a spirited black stallion. Jack rode the stallion until he was acquainted with the horse's speed and gait. Then he cantered over to Portsmouth Square alone.

Here was the city's only voting place. Hundreds of people milled around enjoying Bryant's free music and free whisky. They pulled back to let the man on the stallion have room. Suddenly Hays spurred the black into a dead run. Lying low over the horse's neck, he charged the bandstand at top speed. The admiring spectators never observed him lift his pistols. They only realized that, in a split second, he had emptied both six-shooters. And every flying bullet had thudded into the wooden steps of the bandstand.

Hays whirled the animal around its hind legs and re-

loaded his guns. Later he repeated the same show of marksmanship.

Shouting rose and spread like wildfire. Few men in San
Francisco did not know about the exploits of the Texas
Rangers. The Colt revolver was acquiring national stature
as a superior weapon. Here was the first captain of the
Rangers to use a repeating pistol—here rode Hays, the
colonel who had fought on both fronts in the Mexican
War! A *bona-fide* colonel too—not of the tinhorn variety
like J. J. Bryant.

San Francisco's population was new. Most were case-
hardened men, but also impressionable men. Previous
pledges were cast aside. The man on the black horse received one ovation after another as he rode through San
Francisco's muddy streets.

Samuel Brannan fairly danced up and down in his
enthusiasm. "We've won now," he chortled. "Bryant can't
top a show like that."

He was right. The returns at noon showed Colonel Hays
in the lead. By sundown his delighted backers were firing
victory salutes.

Sheriff Jack Hays! He wrote Susan to leave at once. His
brother Bob returned to Texas to help her prepare for the
trip. Back came Susan's reply as quickly as steamboat
service allowed. Samuel Maverick had served the Hayses
well in disposing of the Texas property. Jack now had the
means to buy a home in California. Let him remember,
urged his wife, that he liked "elbow room" and horses. It
was all right to serve a crowded city as its sheriff, but Susan
knew that her husband would never be comfortable in
close quarters. She would reach California sometime that
September. Let him have everything ready for her arrival.

A draft from Attorney Maverick reached him by next mail. Hays explored the surrounding country for suitable land. This role as sheriff was only temporary; he had never promised anything else. He had nursed only one permanent ambition since his twentieth year, since he had first observed how Spanish-born *ranceros* managed their herds. California had been a pastoral country too. A man had only to ride a few miles from San Francisco's teeming limits to find the same rolling plains that Hays had learned to love in Texas. He bought two thousand acres of undeveloped land down the peninsula. Such property was reasonable. The other thousands of migrants pouring into California dreamed-of gold strikes. Hays put such thoughts out of his mind. Let him fulfill his obligations as sheriff, help bring law and order to the West Coast, and then lay out his quiet, peaceful eixstence as a *ranchero*.

Such an idyllic existence had to be earned. He had to prove himself as a sheriff first. He appointed five deputies, including the loyal Caperton. Carefully he distinguished between the responsibilities of county law and the municipal police.

He had to do that, for the "city law" was still controlled by gamblers. Brannan and associates had gotten nowhere in their bid for control of municipal government. But, as Hays pointed out to his supporters, those men in city hall were duly elected officials. He could not interfere in their jurisdictions. The job of sheriff had limitations as well as responsibilities.

He knew, as did everyone else, when the Brannan-led group secretly formed their Vigilante Committee. "The Hounds" fell apart as a civic menace but the "Sydney Ducks" redoubled their depradations. They set costly fires to cover their burglaries and other crimes. Six times that year major conflagrations threatened the destruction of downtown San Francisco. When indignant merchants filed charges against specific individuals at city hall, those charges were dismissed. Or else no warrants were served.

Vigilantes, acting secretly, took an Australian convict out of the city jail and hanged him. Next, the hooded men closed in on James Stuart. This criminal was seized aboard a vessel in the harbor and hanged from a derrick on the Market Street wharves.

This was lawlessness too—however much the sheriff might sympathize with the committee's founders. He minced no words about his attitude toward the hooded men: Let none of them interfere with him or his deputies. Privately he hoped such a showdown never came.

But it was almost inevitable, especially when the city authorities despaired of combatting the Vigilantes themselves. It was an ironic situation. Now it was San Francisco's city government calling for outside help to bring "law and order." They appealed to the governor, John McDougal. The Vigilantes were holding Samuel Whittaker and Robert McKenzie for their own brand of justice. Next to the executed Stuart, Whittaker and McKenzie were "kingpins" of "The Ducks."

McDougal sent Hays a writ ordering that the two men be taken from the Vigilantes and held in custody for formal trial.

What would Hays do about such an order? Samuel Brannan and the other founders of the Vigilante Committee had elected him. They had supported all of his official acts. Could this be a plot by the city's criminal ring to involve Vigilantes and sheriff in a war of their own?

Hays considered so, but he had his oath to keep. He refused the help of a posse the governor sent from Sacramento. If he must defy the Vigilantes, he would do it in ordinary course of duty.

John Caperton insisted on accompanying him to the Vigilante Committee's headquarters, where twenty-nine men were guarding the two prisoners.

A burly blacksmith, John A. Steele, opened the door. Jack and Caperton stepped inside quickly. Steele caught Caperton's arm.

"Turn him loose," ordered Hays, "and don't resist me. I'm sheriff of this county and anyone who interferes with me is violating the law."

Steele stepped back. Hays had chosen to raid the headquarters in early morning, long before daylight. Most of the guards were sound asleep. So were the prisoners, but Caperton pulled the two "Ducks" to their feet. Van Nokkelen, chief of the committee's secret police, burst into the room.

"Sheriff, are you crazy?" he demanded. "We outnumber you twelve to one."

"Yes," answered Hays, "but none of you wear a star."

A six-shooter in each hand, he motioned Caperton to lead out the prisoners. Then Hays backed slowly from the room. The Vigilantes made no move to attack them.

But, two days later, the committee's hooded men struck the county jail while Hays was in Sacramento. Thirty-six Vigilantes stormed the jail, and twenty minutes later Whittaker and McKenzie were dangling from heavy redwood beams thrust out of the town hall windows.

Hays did not hesitate. He filed charges against members of the committee, including Brannan. All of them posted bail.

The grand jury convened. Grimly the sheriff repeated his charges. The jury no-billed every defendant.

The Vigilantes were in control of the city, and no doubt about it. Now what would they do if Hays offered himself for a second term? He stood openly opposed to them. He had dared file charges against them. When a candidate announced against him, Charles M. Elleard, Hays privately decided that his official days were numbered. But he kept his name in the race.

On the day of election the committee flooded San Francisco with copies of this proclamation:

I offer [announced Stephan Payhran, president of the committee], with the concurrence of my colleagues, the thanks of the Committee to Sheriff Jack Hays for his perseverance, skill, and assiduity. As a public servant he has shown much to commend, and at all times henceforth the Committee will assist him in his legitimate course of office. May he long serve the state of his adoption and receive the good wishes of his fellow citizens.

With that dramatic announcement of its support of Hays for re-election, the Vigilante Committee passed out of existence. Their hooded policemen were no longer needed.

Jack Hays had finished his job in the taming of another frontier. There could not be yet another. Against this one lapped the waters of the Pacific Ocean.

16

The Hunter Home from the Hills

Yes, the Vigilante war was over. But would Jack Hays let roots grow deep enough under his feet to hold? His wife, Susan, wondered that more than once as she stared at the waves in the wake of the good ship *Columbus*.

Bob Hays capably handled most of the details of moving, and sailed with her from Indianola on October 4. Even so, Susan was tired, farewell parties in her honor had lasted a full week. She was grateful for the smooth voyage.

On December 7, 1850, the *Columbus* moved to her moorings in San Francisco harbor. Sheriff Hays did not wait for the passengers to come down the gangplank; he rowed out in a skiff and clambered up a rope ladder. He cooked his wife's first meal in California himself.

Their peninsula ranch was called "Mountain Home." The surrounding hills, however, did not compare with those sheltering San Antonio from prairie northers. The house itself was roomy, but drafty and difficult to make homelike. Susan was not unhappy to learn that her husband regarded this purchase as an investment, not a permanent home.

She yearned to be "settled." Did he? He said so again and again. He continued to be restless, but showed no dis-

paign. This wasn't the Pedernales. But Governor Alfred Cummings of the Utah Territory tendered an official appointment and leading California citizens urged the ex-Ranger to accept.

Susan herself contributed the clinching argument.

"You know you want to go, dear," she said gently. "You've never yet refused a call to help protect your fellow citizens. And you've been very good about your domestic responsibilities for a long time."

He studied her for a moment, then nodded.

There were 587 volunteers willing to follow the ex-Ranger after the elusive young Winnemucca. But they were not Rangers. Hays had an excess of both officers and capable enlisted men. He had not hand-picked these men. He had not required that recruits gallop past a tree trunk and fire ten accurate shots in a matter of seconds. These men came from everywhere and Hays had to accept them as they were.

They were not even tested under fire. He found that out with an experiment on the Carson River.

His volunteer troop was in camp. Jack stole up to a blazing campfire and tossed in a can of sealed fruit. The explosion sent coals and ashes flying. Meanwhile, back in the shadows, Hays whooped like an Indian.

Some of the volunteers cocked their rifles and pistols and stood ready for grim action. But most fled in panic. It took the colonel and his few dependable officers most of the night to reassemble them.

Six hundred green men would get nowhere, decided Hays. How could such a force track down an elusive foe? He could hardly send the mass of men home, but he did pick out thirty who showed courage, horsemanship, and

position to leave the bay region. Its fascination for him never wavered.

And he spent almost every night at home. The thirty-mile ride from "Mountain Home" to his office seldom fazed him. Once home, he was helpful and attentive. Seldom did he mention the risks of his duties. Susan learned from others about such exploits as his clash with Captain Ned Wakeman of the *New Orleans*. The frigate started to clear the harbor without permit. Hays boarded the vessel alone and vowed to shoot any man who moved to lift anchor. The escape of seventeen convicts from a prison brig threw San Francisco into temporary panic. The sheriff pursued them into the mountains near Tulare, recapturing ten.

But such feats only added to an already ample reputation. Sheriff Hays realized their real worth. He had not moved to California merely to acquire more fame as a fearless man with a gun. He rode San Francisco's hilly streets fully aware that he was accomplishing very little in a material way. He was a colorful citizen, yes, and a most valuable one. But he must grow into a substantial citizen too.

A gold-mining venture failed. Then the hunter found his long-sought opportunity. Just across the bay from San Francisco lay eleven leagues of rolling land known as the Peralta Grant or *Encinal*. Hays knew about surveying land grants direct from the Spanish king. He had helped divide such *porcións* in Texas.

A friend, John Clar, proposed a partnership to buy the tract from Vicente Peralta. Clar had an option but little money. Hays disposed of his peninsula land and the deal was made.

But the arrival of John Caperton Hays delayed their

move from "Mountain Home." The son was born August 25, 1852. Gifts poured in for the sheriff's first-born. One package arrived somewhat tardily. From the Texas prairies came a fine gold goblet and two gold spoons. The donor— Buffalo Hump, a Comanche war lord! They had not forgotten "Devil Jack" along the Pedernales.

After long months Hays and Clar cleared all title difficulties to the Peralta Grant. The sheriff had devoted every spare moment to the new promotion. Now the partners could actually sell tracts and mark off a wharf. Plans that had existed on paper or in their visions took physical form. San Francisco newspapers announced the formal establishment of a township across the bay. As yet there were no streets or even businesses—merely a maze of surveyors' stakes and the foundation of wharves. The founders named the city "Oakland."

To Susan's delight, her husband became active in other bay affairs. There was no doubting this permanency any longer. Oakland began to take shape. Every dollar that could be saved from his sheriff's income went into its building. He must still lead a double life, for the second income was needed. He resigned as sheriff on June 18, 1853, but only to accept appointment as United States Surveyor-General of California.

In the next four years he would survey more of California than any other man, but still he managed to keep active in San Francisco affairs. He partially overcame his distaste for public appearances. He represented Texas in a pageant memorializing Henry Clay. He took the lead in organizing the Mendocino and Clear Lake Hunting Club. He attended wedding parties and other social events on Nob Hill, the city's most fashionable section. He even

"gave" a bride away there—his wife's sister. She married his faithful ex-deputy, John Caperton.

Another small saving went into a mining investment. It paid off—almost twenty thousand dollars. A modest sum for the California gold fields, but a bonanza to a struggling family. It meant more could be done about building Oakland.

Richard Hays was born April 29, 1855. The growing family presented a temporary hardship, for Hays had decided against a large residence in Oakland. His image of a home was taking definite shape—a segment of the Peralta Grant. A daughter Kitty was born; but she died two years later. Mary Susan took her place in the growing household.

On February 19, 1859, Hays resigned as Surveyor-General. The Oakland properties now required his full time. A steamship crossed the bay every hour to connect the new town with San Francisco. Ground had been marked off for Durant College. When he could spare the time, Hays galloped his Appaloosa to the site of their future ranch home. Susan approved of the place and named it "Fernwood." A sturdy foundation was laid and timbers cut.

Jack Hays was forty-three years old that April. He did not look it, or act it. When the Paiute Indians went on the warpath in nearby Virginia City, the San Francisco newspapers editorialized that he should command a volunteer force against the Indians:

"The election of a man like Hays, of a national reputation as an Indian fighter and an honest man, will have a very great and favorable influence. Many men will contribute for the expedition, both in supplies and personal services, who otherwise would not."

Hays shook his head: he was too old for another cam-

shooting ability. Let the main force move around on indefinite maneuver. They would hold the Paiutes' attention, at least, while Hays' mobile crew maneuvered into attacking position.

The first skirmish came at a place called Big Meadows. The Paiutes thought to dismay the white men with their sweeping mounted sorties, but Hays had weathered attacks by superior riders. These Rocky Mountain Indians did not hold a candle to the Comanches. The fewer white men carefully avoided being caught in the Indian pincer-like charges. The Paiutes were hurled back time after time.

But these thirty volunteers were little better than the first company Hays had led against red men. His force could not unleash the furious deadly countercharge with which his Rangers had annihilated Comanche forces. There was no crushing young Winnemucca as Yellow Wolf had been destroyed.

But the dogged pursuit wore out the Paiutes. And up marched 212 army regulars under Captain James Stewart. The white men now outnumbered the Indians four to one. Colonel Hays kept the main force pressing in on Winnemucca while he led another picked company across a short stretch of desert. Sooner or later the Paiutes had to turn back to the Truckee River for water. The task force rode through a cold drizzle, recalling memories of the chase after Santa Anna in the Mexican mountains. The Paiutes were turned back from the Truckee and forced to give battle. The army regulars moved into the fight with telling effect. Winnemucca lost near forty warriors in the long skirmish. Eleven white men were killed or wounded. More vital, the Indians had to seek flight in the wasteland again.

They could choose the desert or the mountains. Most of them scattered into the hills and Colonel Hays decided that he could abandon the fight. Certainly two hundred troopers could handle the dispersed Paiute force.

Besides, the home at "Fernwood" was only half finished. Now Jack Hays was as impatient as his wife to dig in roots.

This ranch estate was all he had dreamed about. Here could be kept horses, some sheep and cattle. An orchard burst into bloom, and feed crops greened the valleys. The coyotes were left undisturbed to yap unchallenged in the hills. The Comanches called the slinky beasts a blessing to man. Jack felt the same way. The mournful wail of a coyote also signified freedom from rats and prairie dogs.

Tragedy struck "Fernwood." Susan died at five and Richard at seven. The deaths came over a period of six years, two in successive years. The birth of Betty, born December 3, 1869, helped sooth the aches.

It was a place where a man could grow old happily. In 1861 Jack realized how time had passed. Suddenly the sons of his friends were marching off to war. Suddenly, too, Confederate officials made overtures toward the ex-Ranger. There was talk of a general's command if he would return to his native South. He shook his head, and firmly. He raised a strong, fearless voice in California politics. He was a Democrat. He spoke out as one. But he never considered service against The Stars and Stripes. Many in California could not understand such a paradox. They could have found a parallel in Texas. In 1861 Sam Houston left the governorship of Texas rather than lead his state into the Confederacy. Hays never spoke out in defense of his unique stand; he could have delivered quite an oration.

Not a mile of the territory west of the Sabine River had been won without his help. Who had done more in the march of "Old Glory" Westward? Could he spend a lifetime taking a flag to the Pacific and then turn against it! No. Regardless of his political convictions—no.

The war never ravaged California. San Francisco continued its amazing growth; the village of Oakland swelled into a bustling city. The Oakland Gas Light Company began service. The city became a continental railroad terminus. The University of California purchased lands nearby. Hays was one of the founders of the Union Savings Bank; by 1870 he was a wealthy man.

The once-shy man grew more convivial. Most of their social life centered around Oakland; but he and Susan were not strangers to gala functions on Nob Hill. Neither was John Caperton Hays, bigger than his father at fourteen, and more handsome. Not all the social invitations to cross the bay were accepted, by any means. Only one San Francisco hostess could count for sure on the attendance of the ex-Ranger. She was Mrs. John McMullin, wife of another hard-riding Texan who had found wealth in California. But as hostess Mrs. McMullin had to watch for one risk. Let her turn her head, and her husband and their most distinguished guest would be sitting together outside in low, earnest talk.

Then, shortly, the same Mrs. McMullin was confronted with another problem concerning the Hays clan. Try as she might, the Nob Hill matron could not convince her daughter, Anna, that John C. Hays was not the only presentable young man in the community.

They were married on November 3, 1880. Jack Hays and John McMullin swapped a reminiscence before the elaborate wedding started. A thought struck Jack as he saw his former rider in slick formal attire: Did McMullin remember the dance the Rangers had attended in San Antonio when there had been one coat to every three men!

By 1882 the Colonel was fading. He had never fully recovered from rheumatism after the Paiute campaign. He was taken from the ranch to spend the rainy season in the Galindo Hotel in Oakland. Death seemed very near for a while, but the old warrior rallied. He wanted to go home.

And back to "Fernwood" he went. His doctors agreed, sure that he was regaining strength.

They were wrong. On April 21, 1883, Hays began gasping for breath in the midst of a nap. His wife, daughter, and daughter-in-law hurriedly came to his bedside. The younger Jack Hays galloped out from Oakland. His father regained consciousness but for a long time seemed unable to talk.

Then suddenly his voice came—clear, even: "John, do you know what it is?"

"Yes," nodded his son. "It's Saturday."

"Yes," the dying man said softly. "San Jacinto Day too."

So it was—the forty-seventh anniversary of Sam Houston's victory over Santa Anna, the beginning of Texas. A smile showed on Jack Hays' face and his eyes gleamed. Was he recalling that challenge of 1836, that stirring which had guided a youth Westward to "fight for his rights"? Was he lost in reverie of the half-century he had lived adventurously and vigorously? Was he racing again down every trail he had ever ridden, through the Texas *brasada*, the rugged mountains of Mexico, the wide deserts of Arizona and California? Were voices calling out to

Captain Jack—the voices of Mike Chevaille, of Sam Walker, of Big Foot Wallace, even Houston himself? If so, they were urging him to ride like the wind; there were so many trails, and so little time.

For at 3:45 P.M. the race was over.

Bibliography

Carroll, Curt. *San Jacinto*, The Steck Company, Austin, 1957.

Dobie, J. Frank. *The Longhorns*, Little & Brown, Boston, 1941.

Gambrell, Herbert. *Anson Jones*, Doubleday & Company, New York, 1948.

Garst, Shannon. *Big Foot Wallace*, Julian Messner, New York.

Greer, James. *A Texas Ranger and Frontiersman*, The Southwest Press, Dallas, 1932.

Hogan, William Ranson. *The Texas Republic*, University of Oklahoma Press, 1946.

James, Marquis. *The Raven, a Biography of Sam Houston*, Halcyon House, New York, 1929.

Reid, Samuel C. *Scouting Expeditions of McCulloch's Texas Rangers*, The Steck Company, Austin (facsimile), 1956.

Rose, Victor M. *The life and Services of General Ben McCulloch*, The Steck Company, Austin (a facsimile), 1958.

Webb, Dr. Walter Prescott. *The Texas Rangers*, Houghton Mifflin Company, 1935.

Wellman, Paul. *The Iron Mistress*, Doubleday & Company, New York, 1951.

Williams, Amelia and Eugence C. Barker, editors. *The Writings of Sam Houston, 1813-1862*, Texas Historical Society, Austin, 1911

Index

188

About the Author

CURTIS BISHOP was born in Tennessee, moved to Texas in his youth, and still lives there. His writing career started early, and by the time he was sixteen he was a newspaper reporter and sports writer. He is the author of more than 30 books for adults and young people dealing with a variety of subjects: sports, westerns, history and biography.